Barking Mad

Tales of Liars, Lovers, Loonies
and
Layabouts

Best Wishes

Brendan Nolan

ALSO BY BRENDAN NOLAN

Phoenix Park a History and Guidebook

The Irish Companion

Barking Mad

Tales of Liars, Lovers, Loonies
and
Layabouts

Brendan Nolan

Fresh Appeal
Dublin

Published by Fresh Appeal 2008
ISBN 978-0-9560810-0-1

Brendan Nolan has asserted his right under the Copyright, Designs and Patents Act 1988 to be identified as the author of this work

First published in Ireland in 2008 by Fresh Appeal
138 Esker Lawns, Lucan, Co Dublin, Ireland
www.brendannolan.ie
email: brendannolan@eircom.net
tel: 00 353 (0)1 628 11 25

Printed in Ireland by Naas Printers, Naas, Co Kildare

For Rita

Acknowledgements

Thanks to Liam Flanagan who insisted the story be told.

Thanks to all in Liffey Sound FM for hosting the stories when they were a mic, a voice and the ear of an intimate stranger.

Thanks to Colette Grant for words of encouragement on the first night at the lectern and for the laughs and the yarns ever since.

Thanks to Michael for production and the original concept of turning ephemerality into something else.

Thanks to Sharon Geoghegan for watching the cascading commas and for help along the way.

Thanks to Peter Kavanagh who was there when the storytelling began.

Thanks to Fiachra Kenny for professional opinion, friendship, family and for not playing *Moon River*, so far.

Not forgetting the production crew of: Luci, Rita, Rory, Kevin, Alison, Sheila, Michelle, Rachel, Josh, Holly, and Leo.

Each week, Brendan broadcasts a new story on Liffey Sound FM the community radio station in west Dublin.
You may hear these stories as they are broadcast, locally, or on the Internet.
Broadcast details and times are to be found on the website: www.brendannolan.ie.
Join our email list on brendannolan@eircom.net and we will send you details of new stories and publications as they happen.

Contents

Licence for a Dead Dog

The licence man called on the same day the dog left Sally's home to die. The dog was a free spirit and unlicensed.

The man said the dog should be licenced; Sally said he didn't need a licence because he was fecked.

"It won't do him any good. He wouldn't need it for long," she said.

But the licence man was new. He wanted to be fair, and just, and the dog was alive and standing there looking at him as if he had two heads. "He needs a licence," the man said.

"Well, you better tell him yourself. I can't bear to bother him with the detail. He's not long for this world."

"How old is he?" asked the man, against his better judgement.

"He's fifteen."

"Did he ever have a licence?"

"Never," declared Sally. "Never needed one until you came down the road."

"In that case, you probably should pay arrears," said the new licence man doubtfully.

"I'm not paying arrears for a dog that's dying!"

"The regulations are quite clear. A dog must have a licence. You need one, and you should pay arrears."

He was warming to the task. He was after all a trained official with the might of the law behind him. This dog would be licenced.

"What is the dog's name?"

"Ask him yourself. He never told me. If he tells you, then I'll pay his licence for him; because not only is he dying; but he's broke."

The licence man asked Sally for the full legal name. "My legal name, or the dog's? Because the dog doesn't have a legal name. He's the dog with no name."

"Yours. For the fine."

Sally told him her name, and he left to call on other houses where suspicious barking came from inside.

Most people told him that the barking he heard when he rang the bell was on the television.

He was told the same thing so often that he began to wonder if a dog show was on some station and he was making a fool of himself by insisting that there was a dog there.

So, he looked through the windows to see what was on the television before he rang the bell.

He looked through the window once too often. In the house at the end, where the newlyweds were enjoying their new status, he was seen peering through the glass by the ecstatic female.

He was chased down the road by the disturbed male and a mongrel alsation called Bill. Luckily for the license man he hopped on a passing bus and was not seen in the town again. Neighbours congratulated the groom for his performance and stamina in the chase.

Sally's nameless dog was the only unlicensed dog he managed to note down before he fled.

The dog went away shortly afterwards and Sally never saw the animal again. It migrated to some dog's graveyard and Sally was sad for a few days but just as glad she no longer had to worry about an expiring animal.

She was surprised some time later to receive an official looking letter. It had that intimidating look that means you are banjaxed if you open it and guilty if you don't.

It was to tell her that she had been fined for keeping an unlicensed animal on the premises, or words to that effect.

It made no difference to Sally for she didn't have the money to pay the fine, or the licence , and since the dog was gone, it no longer seemed to matter.

She threw the letter in the fire and that was the end of it for a while.

Somebody asked her, in the weeks that followed, if she would like a pup to make up for the loss of the dog; but the dog was never her's in the first place, so she said no, without explaining why.

It was brought home one night by her son. He was the worst for wear after a stag party for a school pal that lasted three days and ended in a broken engagement, stitches, and returned presents.

He never called it anything other than the dog and when he emigrated to Australia he left the dog in his bedroom to mind the place for him in case he came back before he intended to.

Sally grew fed up with the dog scratching itself in the bedroom at night. One warm sleepless night she hunted the dog downstairs where he remained as a sort of guard dog to the otherwise empty house.

Nobody would rob the house said Sally because there was so little in the place that a burglar would have to bring something with him to steal.

A while after that, when Sally had well forgotten the dog, the man and the letter, a Garda arrived seeking Sally by name.

She said: "That's me. What do you want?"

Sally was in contempt of something or other and was now called upon, by way of a summons, to attend court on a given day at a given time to explain the matter to the presiding judge.

"Do I have to go?" she asked the garda.

He said she had to go and he listened for a good while as Sally explained how the dog had arrived in her life and how it had departed.

But she still had to go to court, he said, and she could explain all she had told him --- in a loud clear voice --- to the justice who would make up his own mind.

It seemed to Sally to be a silly thing to have to do; but she had better go and tell the justice the story and put it all to rest once and for all.

She presented herself in the court on the appointed day and almost missed her name being called out.

She had only ever seen court cases on television and thought she would be placed in the dock for all to see and she was not looking forward to that.

But all she had to do was stand up at the front and face the justice. It was a little like being in school and being asked to explain to the teacher and the class why she had not done her homework.

Just the same, she faced forwards as she did not want to see everybody else looking at her.

The judge listened as she explained that the dog was never hers in the first place; that it wasn't even her son's dog.

He had found it and had given it a good home and now he was in a new home in Australia and she could hardly post the dog to him there. So she had fed the dog until it was fecked, and she apologized for saying feck to the justice but he said it was alright and to continue.

Sally told him the dog left home on the day the man called and was never seen again.

For all she knew it had gone back to where it came from and was only on holiday in her house.

But she was prepared to pay for a licence for one day, the day the man called, but that was it. "A dead dog doesn't need a licence," Sally declared. Her offer was fair. A day was enough to pay, too much really; but still.

However, the judge said a living dog needed a licence and he fined Sally a sum that was more than she could pay and told her to get a licence for the dog, for one year, even though it was missing, presumed dead. She had admitted to the court that the dog stayed with her and so it should have been licensed.

He told her she would go to jail for a month if she did not pay the fine and asked did she understand that? She said she did and did he understand that she had no money, and no dog?

A friendly garda intervened before she was locked up for contempt of court by the judge and took Sally outside the building where she could get some air. He escorted her home in a squad car and it was agreed that she would call into the station every week with something off the fine, until it was paid.

Since Sally had no money to spare beyond her living expenses, she gave up calling in to say she had no money, so a squad car called to her every Saturday to see if she was paying anything this week?

As the weeks passed, without Sally finding any spare money, and with jail consequently looming over a license for a dead dog, an older sergeant in the station started a weekly collection for a "Good Cause."

Anyone who arrived at the public counter was encouraged to place some coins in the collection tin. Few refused the sergeant with the smiling collection box.

The box filled up. The fine was eventually paid, anonymously, and one sunny Saturday the squad car delivered an official licence for an animal named Dawg to Sally's home.

She framed it and hung it on the wall of her son's bedroom so she could tell him, if he ever came home, that the dog was up in the bedroom if he was looking for it.

Only this time it was climbing the wall.

As for herself, she gave up betting on greyhounds and stuck to horse racing. She'd had enough of the life of dogs.

At least you knew where you were with horses.

There was little chance of a stray horse ending up in the spare bedroom and of some fool looking for a licence for it when it was ready to ride off into the sunset.

Still, in a way, she missed the dog. And there were evenings when she found herself calling it in for the night.

But it wasn't there. licence or no licence.

.

Mandrake the Magician

Some people are magicians, some people are magic and some people chance their arm as far as they can throw it or as far as they are let.

It's hard to believe now, with so many multi-screen cinemas open for choice and with high rates of cinema attendance being recorded everywhere; but cinemas in Ireland faced a challenge from television, a few years ago, when cinemagoers stayed away in droves to watch what was then the novelty of television.

Cinema owners tried out different attractions to woo the customers back. Some put in new seats; some allowed booking for Sunday nights in your favourite seat --- no more queuing --- some added extra performances, some even opened on Saturday mornings to show cartoons to children.

Others embraced a mix of reality performance and film long before Simon Cowell or Big Brother became household names on television.

It was called cine-variety and it was a beast of many colours.

You got to see real people performing on a make-shift stage and later you saw celluloid heroes dramatising life, as we never knew it, on the screen.

For a while, it seemed that Utopia had arrived in our home town.

Professional performers were booked --- fresh from a tour of Ireland --- wherever that was, to top the bill at the Grove cinema on the bank of the Liffey in a grand extravaganza of film and razzamatazz.

They came on with wild and impossible introductions.

But they knew tricks of the trade that saw them project their presence right up to the back of the balcony.

They were professional performers, in a cinema, where we could pay a few coppers and enjoy a world of astonishing glamour. We were enthralled.

When it was announced that none other than Mandrake the Magician was to top the bill our wonderment knew few bounds.

There was an American cartoon strip running in a national newspaper at the time featuring a professional magician by the name of Mandrake who got into, and out of, all sorts of scrapes while he solved crime on the side, as you do.

That he might be a real person had not occurred to us. He was real enough in the paper; but that was in your head.

What was certain was that he was coming to perform and we were going to be there.

Whether he was going to perform conjuring tricks or catch a crook was something about which we were quite unsure. But, we travelled in hope.

As it happened, the ambassador from the state of Italy has lived in Lucan for many years.

One such holder of the office was a film enthusiast who liked nothing better than to wait until the main film had begun to slip in and to sit at the back without ceremony.

There was no such thing as personal security or protocol to be observed. The man liked to go to the pictures after work and that was that.

Staff at the Grove were accustomed to seeing him arrive insist on paying for his ticket, buying some sweets and being shown discreetly to a seat.

Soft-drink dispensers were unheard of at that time. If somebody wanted to buy an orange drink they were handed a glass bottle with the cap removed with a bottle opener. A drinking straw was inserted into the sweet liquid to suck the drink through.

The bottles were re-useable and were returned to the bottlers in wooden crates, to be used once more. This was real re-cycling when re-cycling was otherwise something you did on a bike when back peddling.

On the night of Mandrake's solitary appearance in Lucan's only cinema, the ambassador decided he too would enjoy a night of cine-variety and so he set off to watch the show. As was his practice, he waited until everybody was seated; but demand was so strong that it was too late to find an empty seat for him when he arrived.

All spaces were sold; such was the interest in seeing a cartoon turned flesh. Or the mind made real.

The busy manager saw him at the door and saw the cashier apologising profusely for the predicament in which they all found themselves.

He apologised to the ambassador and said had he but known he would have reserved a seat for such a valued customer. The manager was no mean diplomat himself, and hoped to run for elected office in the future, on the county council.

The ambassador, schooled in diplomacy, assured everybody that it was the ambassador's fault entirely. He should have had the foresight to book a seat for such a wonderful occasion in the history of the Grove.

He said that if he were at home and wished to visit a fine theatre he would have had make a reservation long beforehand, and as for reserving a box from which to observe a performance why that would take even longer.

It was the mention of the opera and a private box that gave the manager an idea.

He said he could offer the ambassador a box upstairs if he did not mind sitting alone through the performance.

The ambassador, clearly delighted at this turn of events, tried to insist he would pay the full cost of such a consideration.

But the manager equally insisted he would not allow the ambassador to do such a thing and personally escorted him upstairs to a completely full balcony.

The ambassador stood watching a bad juggler dropping balls, and blaming his props for the hamfisted performance while the manager went away to return with an empty wooden mineral bottle box. The ambassador was to sit at the back of the aisle on the upended box where he had a clear view of what was to happen next with Mandrake.

He took it; for a box was a box, and politics is the art of the possible. For the future, he noted that when reserving seats anywhere, he would specify a seat with arms and a cushioned bottom.

Mandrake, it turned out, was fresh from a tour of Ireland, as we expected, or whatever part of it he hailed from.

He was no American detective but was a native son with accent to match.

Nonetheless, he performed conjuring tricks well and everybody clapped when he produced umpteen different bunches of flowers in impossible colours and threw them to the floor where they buried themselves in the quivering wood with the ferocity of a well-thrown spear.

It went on like that for a while and people were getting a little restless, for when you have seen one bouquet of flowers flying through the air, you have seen a few.

Then Mandrake produced the kettle. This kettle was a magic kettle that could turn milk into stout, or stout into milk, he explained. He demonstrated this apparent miracle, several times, and happy with his handiwork went for the big finish.

He called for a volunteer member of the audience --- who would know the difference between stout and milk --- to come forward and to taste one, and then the other, and confirm that magic had occurred here on the stage in the Grove in Lucan this night.

A burly chap whom few of the audience recognised flung himself forward as volunteer.

There was no stage in the Grove. It was, after all, a cinema, in more tranquil times.

So, a temporary platform was placed below and in front of the screen, extending towards the audience. Sheets of plywood formed a front of sorts to the stage and some steps led from the auditorium to the performing area, in anticipation of audience participation.

But the volunteer became carried away with his moment of fame. He stood below the steps and waved to the audience who waved back, cheered, or booed, according to their disposition.

When he had milked the attention for whatever it was worth, he caught hold of a large sheet of plywood to vault up onto the stage.

But the plywood had been tacked together on the understandable premise that it was all temporary, anyway. The structure was not designed for abseiling idiots.

16

The plywood gave way and the man fell backwards, as might be expected.

A large directional spotlight on the platform facing towards Mandrake came down with the man and was damaged in the fall. Mandrake, forgetting his stage persona, for the moment, told the man that he was an idiot.

He said the steps were there for accessing the stage and who did the man think was going to pay for the lamp; a lamp that had been paid for by Mandrake himself, not the cinema ?

While the surprised volunteer lay on his back thinking about not having a free pint, the pain in his back, his lost dignity and the prospect of having to pay for a lamp that no longer worked, a lone voice called out from the balcony.

"If Mandrake is magic, he should be able to wave a wand and fix the lamp."

Somebody else shouted that the idiot should pay for the poor man's lamp, and pretty soon the entire audience was happily divided into the Mandrakians and the Idiots. Nobody was neutral. Everybody had an opinion.

A wonderful night was had by all, with the possible exception of Mandrake, whom we never saw again, or the idiot, for that matter.

Certainly, the ambassador from Rome must have thought he was back in the Coliseum with a crowd roaring for blood.

But it was only Lucan on a good night contemplating the world of make-believe and observing the passing of time.

It was magic.

Walking Corpse

It's not too often that a man walks out to his own funeral. Most of the time, a person dies and that's it. Somebody else worries about the coffin and the hearse and nice flowers and burial and sandwiches and tea for the hungry mourners afterwards.

Sometimes, there is a little caterwauling for the dead soul and its passing; but not so much in recent years. People have become too busy for that sort of behaviour.

It would be thought you were losing the run of yourself if you began howling like a banshee in November, the month of the dead.

Charley lived in the town all his working life. He was never much trouble to anybody and passed away as he lived; quietly and without much fuss.

He even managed to walk out to the hearse when it became clear that recent renovations to the small terraced house in which he had died meant he could not be passed out the window in his present state.

Charley passed away while evening television was on. He didn't even interrupt the ads. So quietly did he expire that his sister-in-law, Maureen, who was sitting in the other good armchair beside him, knew nothing of his passing until she asked if he might like some tea before he went to bed?

When he did not answer she took it he was in one of his moods and went off to put the kettle on for herself.

It was only after a while that she realised Charley was quieter than usual and Maureen worried if she had been too quick when she said he couldn't watch highlights of the match, instead of her favourite soap.

It was after all, half his house. The other half belonged to Maureen and to her sister Betty who was Charley's wife for several decades. So, Maureen chatted away to the back of Charley's head for several more minutes while she waited for the kettle to boil.

When it did, she made enough tea for both of them and then discovered Charley would drink no more tea on account of he was dead.

Gone.

Without saying a word to anybody, he just gave up the ghost.

Maureen shook him and shouted at him for a while as if she could call him back from the other world. She recalled an out-of-body documentary she had half watched last week and tried to remember just how the soul had returned to the body in that case.

Maureen looked up at the ceiling for inspiration and shouted Charley's name as if he would come clattering down the stairs to make everything right again.

She tried to work out when Betty would come home so she could tell her that Charley was dead. It all seemed a bit abrupt for Maureen, and for a while she considered going to bed and letting Betty find out for herself.

After all, there are some things best shared between husband and wife.

But then she decided she would wait up and tell Betty herself.

Charley had been a good man. He had lived with two sisters for a long time and allowed them continue their family life in the same way as before he had arrived as a lodger in the top back room.

The only difference was that he slept with Betty in her bed after they married and Maureen had occasion to comment to Betty, at least once a week, that the springs on her bed were designed for sleeping on, and not much more.

Charley said he liked to test them well in case they were ever needed for anything else, and Maureen calmed herself with thoughts of her small garden and how she might plant something nice there herself.

Fresh air was always good for a person and was never wasted; but Maureen found she was getting a little too much fresh air in the early days. But, like her garden, things settled down after a while.

One winter, Charley declared that the wooden sash windows should be replaced with modern aluminium windows that required little cleaning and no annual painting at all.

19

Everybody on the road was getting in new windows and if they didn't do the same, their house would stick out like a sore thumb the salesman assured them as earnestly as a repentant sinner at the doors of heaven.

That was Charley's downfall. The windows.

The front door of the terraced house opened from the outside into a square hall that was the size of the open door squared.

Because of the size and shape of the hallway, it was neither possible to remove Charley from the sitting room by way of the door nor by way of the window which was now devoted to a large pane of glass with a small opening at the top for air, and appearance only. The glass was surrounded by well inserted aluminium. It would not be removed without determined assault.

Normally, and in times past, when a person died in their bed upstairs the windows were removed to allow safe passage of the coffin with the corpse in it. The local coalman pulled his lorry up onto the path while the neighbours prayed out loud, in case of swearing being heard from the men manhandling the deceased, and the wooden coffin.

There were no gardens in front of these houses so the lorry and the men could get in against the wall with no difficulty.

Strong hands caught the coffin and lowered it on to the bed of the lorry and then off the lorry and into the yawning hearse and that was the end of the house part of the removal.

But, Charley died downstairs in the room to the right of the front door and a coffin would not manoeuvre out the door because of the restricted shape of the hall.

The undertaker ever the professional problem-solver had a practical word with the priest and with the grieving Betty who was a big woman and mighty in her black-robed grief, now that she had gotten over her first shock.

She had only stepped out for a few minutes and Charley had gone off without her, and so she was uncertain whether to weep gently or throw herself upon the coffin in grief. For now, she was quiet and dabbed at an eye with a small handkerchief.

It was agreed to manoeuvre Charley's coffin out the door with as much respect as possible. The long box could not move out in a horizontal position so it had to go out in an vertical manner.

Around this time sister-in-law Maureen decided she had been remiss, somehow, and she had better make sure Charley was treated well, on the way out of his home.

It took the undertakers some time to re-assure her that when they placed one end of the coffin on the floor they were absolutely certain Charley was standing on his two feet and not on his head.

Maureen didn't want him getting dizzy in there with the blood rushing to his head, she said. They said they understood and would make sure that Charley would not faint.

They wobbled the end of the upright coffin to the left, then they wobbled the coffin to the right and finally they were able to lay Charley back down again on the ground. Six men lifted him and his coffin shoulder high and walked out to the hearse.

Charley loved walking, and he was the only man in the town who ever walked out of the house to his own funeral.

He was buried the next day, and far as anybody knows he's still above in the graveyard.

Maureen was sorry she had not bought a video camera out of the new Argos catalogue and they could have filmed the funeral.

Charley would have loved that. They could have watched it on the telly.

Together, with a nice cup of tea.

Plucking the Turkey

At a time when you can order a dead turkey over the internet and expect the man in the van to deliver it to you in time for Christmas it's worth recalling when most people kept a fowl or two around the place for profit or just to feed the family.

Hens were kept for their free-range eggs and were allowed to freely peck their way along the footpath or the roadway; the only daylight danger being from a speeding bicycle and a reckless rider cycling with malice aforethought.

After dark was another matter. Several families kept a licensed firearm to hand for firing in the air at the sound of a sniffing fox.

And sometimes, a shotgun blast rent the still mid-winter air when a family had no fowl to take care of. Sometimes it was just a father discouraging human foxes from calling on a likely chicken of a daughter.

In any case, many families added a few turkeys to their flock for the Christmas market.

There were men who made a few shillings by calling to the growers in the weeks before Christmas and dispatching the turkeys in situ.

There was little nicety about the matter, the neck was rung and the bird was hung up for plucking of feathers and another bird was grabbed as the men worked their way through the terrified gabble.

Until all was quiet for another year.

Plucking was another matter and there was the issue of disposing of feathers afterwards. Feathers and other disposables were left wherever it was convenient to do so and never mind the environment which had not been invented.

It was a time before plastic bags took over the world and any convenient cardboard box from the local shop would do to carry away a few feathers, once a year.

Large plastic bags were unheard of at the time; so Matt the foreman in the builder's providers yard asked the coalman for the loan of a few real coal bags for a week.

He wanted to pluck some Christmas turkeys and dispose of the feathers, before returning the bags.

The coalman was wary of civilians asking for a loan of the tools of his trade, since few people would ask a brain surgeon for a lend of a scalpel to cut a piece of twine.

People had no respect for a good coal bag. They just didn't understand.

But he gave Matt five empty bags on the condition that they be returned and ready for transporting coal for home fires in the short dark days before Christmas.

A week passed and Matt handed back the bags, as promised. He even straightened them out so there was a suspicion that they had been ironed; though that was probably a fancy.

It wasn't until the following week that the bags came to be used for delivering coal, in the usual way.

There was a man living in the area who was in receipt of as many disability benefits and charitable donations as he could get his hands upon, on account of his alleged blindness.

Alfred was visually impaired, to an extent, and deserving of a degree of support to ease any difficulties he might encounter as he went about his daily chores.

Depending on who was the charitable giver, Alfred exaggerated his lack of sight until he could see nothing at all, according to himself.

People who knew him had a vague idea that all he needed was a pair of strong glasses; but were too polite to say anything.

After all, if a man says he can't see, then they'd take him at his word, until he proved otherwise; though he was never included in the darts team at Christmas.

Alfred, a bachelor, kept a cat for company, for he didn't like dogs. His alleged blindness served him well when his current cat entered the garden next door.

The woman in there had believed during the previous Christmas that the price being asked for turkeys in the shops was so exorbitant that she would rear her own the following year.

Not only that, but she would show a profit on the effort.

So, she bought four young turkeys and badgered her husband into converting a shed at the bottom of the garden into a turkey house. The turkeys wrecked her garden as they grew but she didn't mind; it was all in a good cause.

She passed the year counting her turkeys and contemplating which would be best to keep for the family when the big day arrived and which she would sell.

Should she sell off the fattest and make the most money, and have a different turkey for the family plate, or, should she keep the largest bird for the household and invite people to visit for turkey sandwiches over the New Year? It was a problem she happily reflected upon whenever the subject of Christmas came up during the year.

It was not to be for a catastrophe occurred when the dead turkeys were hung up in the shed after the visit of the turkey strangler.

The hanging turkeys were attacked overnight by a fox and rendered useless for human consumption thereafter. At least, the good woman and her husband were told so by Alfred, who claimed extraordinary hearing on account of his poor vision when he heard a fox passing by the night before.

In doing so, he was giving the fox a bad name; for the local fox had not been near the turkeys at all; it was Alfred's cat that was at fault.

A fact that Alfred could attest to since he had seen the cat as it was about to pounce on the dead birds but was unable to call out since he was not supposed to be able to see.

If it got out that he could see well enough to observe the stalking cat at a distance in the dark, then his benefits would diminish.

The dead turkeys could not be eaten nor could they be sold. Lots of discussions went on but the dead turkeys remained compromised.

In the midst of all the cackling, Alfred made a note not to call in there in the days between Christmas and New Year when he might be offered a gallon of turkey broth to take home as a special treat.

He also avoided the wild woman who was on the hunt for the offending fox every night since her turkeys had been attacked. She borrowed a shotgun from her cousin in the next town, the guy who kept springer spaniels and who never trusted Alfred.

Alfred knew instinctively that it was safer to stay indoors and to keep the cat under wraps, at least for a while.

In the days that followed, and as Christmas music drove everybody to distraction in the shops, it happened that one particular benefactor was moved to send Alfred five bags of coal so he could stay warm over Christmas.

This benefactor seemed to equate Alfred's lifestyle with that of a Charles Dickens' urchin who had to leave his home to walk through the snow in blind pursuit of firewood to stay warm and alive.

The reality was that Alfred could hardly stir out of his comfortable house for fear of missing yet another van delivery of something for the Christmas from well-wishers.

Alfred's plausibility when he was in form was such that he could have been elected Pope without first becoming a priest, had he put his mind to it.

So, when the coalman and his helper arrived with the five bags of coal Alfred was hard put to move enough goods out of the way so as to allow the men access through the hallway of his terraced house to the back yard.

He went with them to oversee the delivery. He would count the sound of the number of bags being emptied. He trusted nobody.

It so happened that the coal bags now in use were the same bags that had been loaned for feather disposal. So, when the first bag was emptied, a flock of feathers started to fall out of the bag as well as the tumbling coal.

The foreman had not emptied the bags of all feathers as promised and they had become pitch black from contact with the coal.

Not only that, but they rose in a swirling miasma in front of Alfred who could only stare at the black blizzard as it fluttered around him.

After all, the sound of a feather falling is the sound of silence.

And since Alfred could not admit to sight of the dancing feathers he had to stay quiet and accept the revenge of dead turkeys as the feathers landed on his head and shoulders like an early Christmas snow from a coal mine.

Somewhere, Alfred fancied he heard the sound of turkeys gobbling with glee at his unexpected windfall.

The cat, wise animal that it was, left home for a while.

The coalman decided against going back to Matt to complain about feathers being left in his bags; for he could hear the jibes even now of his coal being as light as a feather.

Coal was coal and feathers were feathers and as to which weighed the most, they could argue that until the turkeys came home for Christmas.

Jesse James Loved my Granny

The outlaw Jesse James wanted to marry my grandmother. Or, at the very least, he wanted to be her very best friend. She was aware of this and politely refused his advances.

Her maiden name was Kelly and he thought she was related to Ned Kelly the Australian outlaw.

Apart from her being an attractive woman, Jesse thought that she would understand where he had come from as a man outside the law.

But she wasn't related to any known desperados; she was just a Lucan woman who was widowed early who thought the postman was a bit odd with his American accent.

Few guessed in Lucan that there was a famous American outlaw in their midst; much less that he was delivering the post to their doors.

The legend is that Jesse James was shot dead by his nephew Robert Ford while hanging up a picture in his home in Missouri. What actually happened was that he was holding a *pitcher* for carrying water… not a picture.

They were target shooting and Jesse was holding the empty pitcher out for Bob to shoot at it. But Bob missed with his pistol shot and killed Jesse's dog by mistake, who was nearby.

Everybody came running when Ford shouted that he had killed the dog and they thought Jesse was dead. But he was not dead. He was just cross at the loss of his dog.

To make up for his bereavement they had a big funeral for the surprised dog, an Irish red setter called Brian.

After the wake and the burial and a few more drinks, Jesse was persuaded that it was an ideal opportunity for Jesse James to cease to exist. He could build a new life for himself in a new land. The hunt for him would go to the grave with Brian, who was past caring about any of it and would tell nobody what really happened.

So, Jesse hid in Ireland with an outlaw pal of his called Pitt, who was returning for a short while to bury some money for his retirement before returning to America.

Pitt was one of the Sandpits off the Strawberry Beds and when he went back to America Jesse took a job as a Christmas postman in Lucan.

Pitt went to Hollywood, instead of Missouri, where he took a job as a cowboy extra on the new western films. Jesse gave him a big white hat that he bought in downtown Lucan as a going away present.

When Pitt retired he left the hat to his grandson Brad who wore it in his first film that featured two women actresses driving around in a car.

Once Pitt was gone, Jesse became homesick for a while. To ease the loneliness he got another dog for company.

He called it Dawg Eile because it was a bitch.

His old dog used to catch the reins of Jesse's horse when Jesse was too drunk after a night in the saloon to lead it home; so Jesse trained Eile to do the same with the postman's bike and the strap of the post bag.

The last thing an outlaw needs is to be found in charge of a postman's bike, while intoxicated.

It was a close run thing on Christmas Eve when Jesse, the bike, and Eile were still delivering the post after dark … having lingered too long in houses where the moonshine flowed before it ever fell dark.

Jesse came upon my grandmother's house on the outskirts of the town. It was in darkness while she was out doing some last minute shopping. Looking at the house and sighing for what would never be, Jesse saw a stranger coming out of the back downstairs window with her festive tree.

Jesse recognised a fellow outlaw, when he saw one. He was a Christmas tree thief.

Knowing no other way, Jesse drew a plastic water pistol he carried with him for shooting at inquisitive dogs to discourage their attentions to Eile when she was in heat.

Given the time that was in it; the pistol was filled now with a strain of poitín that would take paint from a door if it spilled on it.

Falling back on his basic training as an outlaw, Jesse James fired and caught the thief in his right ear with a stream of firewater.

It is a well known fact that if you lose control of your inner ear you will fall down on your ear and so it happened.

The man lost his equilibrium and fell with the Christmas tree on top of him.

Jesse, seeing the man was confused by the singing in his ear whipped the official postal belt off the bike and tied him up.

Against his better instincts, Jesse delivered the tree thief to the garda station. But first, he hid the tree in my granny's garden so it would be safe and he could restore it for her on his return and win a little attention.

He told the officer in charge that he found the man on the road with a stolen Christmas tree in his possession.

Jesse surrendered the thief to the Garda and left as soon as he could. There was a lingering doubt in his mind that he might be recognised somehow.

He went back to find my grandmother had returned to find her Christmas tree in the garden. She had set the tree back up in the house herself being a woman that took everything in her stride.

Jesse told her what happened when he got there and was invited into the small house, but just for a minute.

She made a strong pot of tea and gave him several USA assorted biscuits with it in case he was lonely for home.

But, when he asked her out after Christmas, she said no.

After all, how could you trust a postman who carried a water pistol in his pocket, who called himself Jesse and had a dog called Eile?

A man who thought his bike was a horse and who freewheeled down Chapel Hill singing *Ghost Riders in the Sky*.

Besides, the story of some man climbing out a window with a Christmas tree was a tale too tall for her.

As for shooting him in the ear with a water pistol, well there were just some stories that defied belief.

Postman or no postman.

Poor Jack's Weather

Rupert Murdoch has affected the local weather a fair bit in recent years. Or, at least, he has been responsible for strange reporting of weather movement in the area.

It's unlikely however that the media mogul knew anything at all about the weather reports being passed on to others by Poor Jack.

Poor Jack was a man much admired for his skill in attracting Lady Luck to his side more often that others.

If Jack bought a ticket for a raffle the chances were it would show up in the winner's lists, sooner or later. So, people naturally tended to want to stand beside him when the lot was cast.

Luck has a way of doing that, rubbing off on you, or so they say.

That's why people travel for miles and miles and burn up lots of petrol to buy a Lottery ticket in a lucky shop, far, far, away. That they never win doesn't seem to matter, for they will head off next time with just as much hope.

Some people wear green socks for the same reason. Some wear odd socks. Others rub relics in the hope of a miracle. Perhaps people do benefit from such behaviour, or maybe they just feel better as a result of calling Luck to their side.

As a side effect of his tendency to win bets placed lots of times, Jack was listened to when he spoke on other matters, unrelated to luck, just in case he might also be right there.

So, when he declared on a fine summer's day, in the middle of something of a drought; that everybody should get indoors --- as soon as possible --- ahead of the torrential rains and flooding that was on the way; many people turned their eyes towards the bonny blue sky above.

The sky was as it had been all day and the day before and the day before that, as blue as any John Hinde postcard ever was.

So, people were puzzled and some asked Jack privately if he had some inside knowledge of weather patterns.

If he had, then quite a few farmers and sellers of outdoor equipment would like to know which way rain would fall in the near future.

Jack insisted that storms were heading this way from the west.

He was pressed by several men on how he knew this not that anybody doubted him; but it hadn't rained in a long while and why should there be a sudden storm it being a Thursday afternoon in high summer; unless the end of the world was nigh?

This was a year when instead of incessant rain, the sun poured down all day, every day, causing sunburn, giddiness and drought.

Wearying of incessant questioning of his foreknowledge, Jack said it had been so announced and confirmed on television.

This confused people even more; because a good many had listened to the radio news --- which included the weather report --- and it had said it would be as fine as ever, with no rain.

People could go to the beach or on a picnic with little fear of a downpour to spoil the day, said the helpful weather person.

Finally, a man called Harry asked Jack to state which station had reported that this dreadful weather was approaching from the west.

Harry always asked direct questions whether it was popular or not.

Jack said, patiently, that recently he had a Sky satellite dish installed on his home so he could watch Sky sports and have a little flutter on some sporting results in other countries.

He had gotten the inside dope on the calamitous weather from the weather reports. If people did not believe him, then that was their problem. He had done his duty to the community by saying what he knew to be about to happen.

And if it sounded awkward, the way he said it, well that was just Jack's way of speaking when he was excited.

Harry wanted to know why a weather report on one station should be no different to another, give or take the antics of the person reporting the weather.

Jack was a patient man and when people approached him to ask who was going to win something soon, he gave his opinion freely. He marked many a man's card before the event. He freely gave advice to several married women seeking a little gambling danger who just might balance the household budget if they won.

Jack was the soul of discretion and a keeper of dreams.

But, luck did not always pass on to the second person and if people lost their entire wager; few blamed Poor Jack for this; they simply put it down to their own bad luck.

Jack explained to Harry, on the subject of the weather, that you had to take the long view on some matters and he was simply telling his neighbours, as a matter of courtesy, that they would be unable to reach home if they did not go there as soon as possible, on account of the flooding that was soon to result from the deluge that was even now on its way.

He explained that the mid-western states of America were suffering a rainstorm that could turn into the second flood, according to breathless reports from television reporters on the streets.

The storm that was causing such depredation in America was proceeding eastwards from the devastated area.

People were being evacuated from their homes and Jack thought people should be aware of that. He said this as a way of emphasising the veracity of his report.

Harry asked what this had to do with Ireland and this town in particular?

Poor Jack replied in slow simple words - that he might use to a child - that Ireland lay eastwards of the United States. The storm would reach Ireland and this town without a doubt, probably this afternoon, if not this evening, or by night time at the latest.

Harry said fair enough and went home to re-write his bet for the next race. It had been based on a Poor Jack tip; but Harry had now changed his mind.

It was obvious that Poor Jack's mind was unravelling, probably on account of the cosmic rays coming into the house from the satellite dish on the gable.

Poor Jack's bet for the day was based on his considered opinion of a particular trainer's method of letting the horse walk when the others were galloping in training.

This, he assured everybody would mean the other horses would be tired and Poor Jack's tip would be raring to go when the race started. In fact, Jack said,. he was going to watch the whole race on his new Sky television himself in his house.

He did so and when the horse lost, by a mile, he shrugged and put it down to the vagaries of horse racing.

He kept a weather eye out the window, for the expected downturn in local conditions, and when it didn't rain and there were no floods, Jack consoled himself with the certainty that he had warned his neighbours and that was all a good neighbour could do.

He thought for a while that he might ring Rupert Murdoch to tell him his weather reports on Sky television were misleading. But he changed his mind and bought a scratch card instead and won the lowest instant prize possible. It was still more than his stake money had been, so that was alright. His treasure chest continued to grow.

In the time that followed, the reporting of a storm that never came affected Poor Jack's standing in the community.

Erroneous reports of rain and flooding that do not come are serious and it's how local oracles are toppled. Jack lost his reputation for perspicacity in all matters, all in a day, over a little rain.

People still asked Poor Jack what he thought might win the national lottery and how he saw the numbers tumbling out. But it was more for an echo of old times than in the hope that he might be right.

He was supplanted as a weather forecaster somewhat by a rival who lived in the far end of the town who was not so much retired as finished work in favour of a state subsidy.

Paul liked the world of weather and its excitement and would listen to the weather report on the radio and step outside his house to wait for somebody to stop to stay hello.

He would gaze into the sky and repeat the weather forecast as if he had divined it himself. What he now said was his own forecast and observation, he said.

He would forecast a little light rain, with improvements later, or a clearance to brighter weather from the west. With no reference to the United States at all, or mid-western flooding of any sort.

People thought him to be good for a while, until somebody noticed a similarity between his reports and the reports they heard on the car radio.

Most people were blue in the face with the weather report on every station, every hour, anyway, as if any of them was going to be any different.

When challenged, Paul gave up the forecasting. He took to cutting his garden hedge and shaping it into the form of a windmill, instead. One that would never move.

That's the problem with the weather, you can't believe anybody. The only sure thing is that it is going to change.

Ask for Poor Jack, he's still backing winners, rain or shine, and he's still worried about the drought in Arizona.

It could rain and flood the desert there, he says; but nobody listens to him anymore.

Nobody has any trust in wise men anymore.

The Undead

Kathleen was a very popular woman in the town and when a notice appeared in the death columns of the paper to say she was dead people were distraught, and thought they should really have done something nice for her, while she was alive.

Some said a prayer for her, others thought they would go to the funeral and others felt it their duty to call to Kathleen's home to say how sorry they were to her husband and their grown-up son.

Others said they didn't know her that well, hadn't got time to call; but felt they needed to do something. A few decided to add her name to the list of goat sponsors for the third world when next the ads were on the radio.

Those that called to her family home to commiserate were surprised to be greeted by the late Kathleen herself at the door.

It happened that there were two women of the same age living in the town; neither off whom was related to the other.

The person that died was known to all as Kay so as to tell her apart from the other Kathleen.

An earlier name given to both of them in school was discarded as soon as possible by both women. Kay was a redhead and was called Rua to mark a difference between her and the other Kathleen who was dark haired and therefore know as Kathleen Dubh.

The names were soon shortened to Rua and Dubh but that led on to many arguments. At one time, the town divided into the Ruas who thought Kay was a gas ticket and Dubhs who thought Kathleen to be a better class of a person altogether.

It's hardly surprising that Rua was the first to be caught smoking while still in school. Or that she was returned to her parents by a garda car on Hallowe'en night the worst for drink and smoke inhalation from the bonfire she had tried to jump across. And failed.

Quite often, when the postman was on holiday and a replacement walked the route, one Kathleen received post for the other.

Given that Dubh was a married lady of probity and Rua was anybody's for a biscuit, it can be assumed that the private correspondence of one did not suit the other.

When Rua died, she did so in impressive circumstances in Spain while in that warm country celebrating the maturing of a man's financial investment.

The man was married to another and when Rua had an unfortunate accident with an oyster the post mortem said it was death by misadventure. Rua would have liked the verdict since she was game for adventure any time. Hit or miss, it made no difference.

Dubh, when she had exhausted the great joke of thanking people for sympathising with her for her death, felt she should attend Rua's funeral and to let bygones be bygones.

The mourners on the day were a mixed bunch. Some were Ruas and some were Dubhs. The Ruas who thought they were at Dubh's funeral for spite were shocked to see Kathleen Dubh herself striding along greeting everybody by name.

When a coffin is closed it's very hard to tell who is inside. And until the practice of placing large photographs of the deceased on the coffin meets wider usage, people will continue to be confused at funerals.

The poor participating priest was taken weak when Dubh smiled back at him from a forward pew when he got to his "I am sincere now" part of his address.

He was not long in the parish and thought the woman in the coffin was supposed to be the woman smiling up at him. That she was not was clear, but who then was in the box?

For a wild moment he thought he had come to the wrong church and was hallucinating.

Then he thought he was being set up in this parish, as he had been in the last one, when some parishioners had him called out on a bogus sick call while he was leading the rosary in the month of May.

He had returned quite flustered to hear Peter from out the Road leading the congregation by intoning the 37th Glorious Mystery wherein St Judas meets St Patrick at Bingo in the Garden after Brigid from Kildare is made Pope.

Somebody had written to the bishop on that occasion and he was on a final warning, though it wasn't his fault.

Then he saw Tommy the Tiler in the congregation who nodded encouragement to him. Once Tommy did that, the good father knew he had a funeral to perform so he lay to with gusto. He switched off the microphone and projected his natural voice to the back end of the balcony. A lot of people could not hear him; but they knew the gist of it , anyway.

Tommy the Tiler had been declared dead twice already, though he was never sick a day in his life. Tommy was a single man and was something of a person of habit who liked to be in a certain part of a certain pub at a given time. On the dot.

But Tommy fell in love for a while with a widow woman who needed a few things done about the house and lingered with her a bit longer than was wise.

It was assumed, quite naturally, that Tommy must be ill not to be in his usual spot at the appointed time and it was only a short step from that to his reported demise and a whipround for a wreath.

Tommy put the matter to rest himself when the widow asked him to paint the outside of her good-for-nothing son's house when Tommy was finished painting hers. He abandoned her and the half-painted house for his place on the barstool.

He had been declared dead by then by popular opinion and he had a job explaining to all that he was still alive.

It happened a second time when Tommy took up jogging after seeing the women's mini marathon on telly and becoming enthused by the human form.

Somebody passing by in a car saw his red face and a few days later he was told by a passerby that he was dead, again, according to best reports.

This time he said he would have to do something about the rumours. So he came to an arrangement with the local undertakers and the church authorities that a cousin of his would confirm his next death, if it was a serious one.

For now, the priest would have to come to a similar understanding with the undead Kathleen. And with anybody else that did not die when their death was reported in the town.

Meanwhile, he had the correct order of the mysteries of the Rosary written out on his wrist so there could be no mistakes.

He said a quick prayer that no more of the undead would turn up in his congregation, today, and lashed into a eulogy for whoever was in the coffin, good, bad, or indifferent.

Given that it was wild Rua in the coffin, he only managed, with his generalisations on how great she was, and everybody's friend, to convince both the Ruas and the Dubhs that he had known Rua a little too well.

From that day on, the good man knew no peace either from the living or the undead. People talked about him and his never-happened affair with Rua. The town divided between the Rua-was-right and Rua- was- a-bitch factions and carried on as before.

Tommy and Kathleen took up with one another now that they had a good deal in common and became quite an item at the Sunday tea dances in the hotel.

Some said they were loving on borrowed time; but they danced a nice tango, and it was lively.

Kathleen's husband was glad she was getting out more nad had a new interest.

It gave him more time to watch sports on televison. In any case, he always felt he had married the wrong Kathleen.

I Kissed Rock Hudson

Frances was a woman who, when the time came, liked to acknowledge it was high summer and for that reason kept a good frock hanging in the wardrobe.

When the days grew longer and brighter and temperatures rose and the grass in the back garden began to get too high Frances would announce to all that if the weather stayed as hot as it was she'd wear the summer frock.

Some people took this to mean that she would put on summer clothes to keep her cool as she pottered around her house. But that was not the case.

Keen observers could see that Frances appeared in just the one frock for the summer season. It was a white cotton sleeveless dress with bright pattern flowers on it.

She made it herself from a piece of cloth she bought as a remnant in a drapery store in Dublin the year she came home from America.

And if the dress fitted her when it was made, it still fitted her; but she no longer fitted the dress.

For she had put on weight in places that to those that favoured a Rubinesque figure was fine; but to people that favoured Victoria Beckham and her few bones, Frances was a little overweight.

Frances had no need to work outside the home since she returned from America in recent years so she had nobody in work with whom to discuss diets and fashions.

It followed that she was very happy in her summer frock.

She was aged somewhere in her 50s, people guessed; but she might have been in her 40s after a hard time in America or she could have been in her 60s and had an easy time in a foreign land.

Nobody was terribly sure, for she came to live in the town with no apparent history other than what she declared about herself.

Frances was not of the town, and so there was neither seed breed nor generation to assess her against. She was herself.

She left Ireland to seek her fortune in America. Having lived in America for years she returned. She never said whether or not she had made her fortune in America

It was assumed that she had made something; for she had no need to work. She spent her days keeping the front garden in a showpiece state while the back garden turned to meadow.

When it got really dense she went and knocked on the door of Old Johnny who owned a retired draught horse called Tony.

And she would say: "Johnny, I need my grass eaten."

And Tony would munch down the grass until Frances was happy. Johnny and Tony were the closest friends Frances had in the town. She received no visitors from anywhere else.

Leaning on the gate one June evening when the western sky was on fire, Frances let it slip very casually to a few neighbours that she had used to live in Beverly Hills.

And she let it be known further that she used to babysit for Rock Hudson.

Anybody that cared to enquire would have discovered that Rock Hudson had no children.

Still, Frances said she was Rock Hudson's babysitter and what's more, on one fine night when Rock Hudson was driving her home and the sweet perfume of summer was in the valley Rock Hudson had stopped at her small house in his large car and when he leaned over to open the door for her he had kissed Frances.

And Frances told her neighbours that --- may God forgive her --- she had kissed Rock Hudson back.

Frances achieved a new respect in the eyes of women who envied her, for Rock Hudson was a matinee idol; and men thought if Rock Hudson saw something in Frances, then Frances needed a bit more study from them than they had given her, so far.

And when Rock Hudson sadly passed away after falling ill, no amount of money or fame could reverse the effect of acquired immune deficiency syndrome or AIDS as it was called by some, that took him away. People said mostly gay people were in danger from the disease at the time.

Frances, when asked how this could be, said had she been still in Hollywood, Rock Hudson would never have been gay.

Since people didn't know Rock Hudson personally and they did know Frances and since she was not known to tell lies people accepted that perhaps what she said was true and that perhaps Rock Hudson had indeed slipped away from a diet that went wrong when slimming became fashionable, as Frances had revealed.

While this was going on and while Rock Hudson was fading from memory Cyril came to live in the town. He set up home not far from Frances.

He was also a man with no past, present, or, future and though he had no obvious source of funds, he did not go to work or sign on or take on odd jobs that people turn their hands to when there is no regular pay packet to anticipate.

But; one evening in talking to neighbours, with an American twang, he let it be known that he knew Tony Curtis , a very heterosexual macho matinee idol.

It seemed like the town was becoming an outpost of Beverly Hills, what with Frances knowing Rock Hudson and Cyril knowing Tony Curtis.

There is a story told by Tony Curtis that when new young actresses came to work in the studios Tony Curtis told them he was their personal kissing coach appointed by the studio. Some even believed him, others turned up for coaching anyway.

Cyril said he was Tony Curtis's kissing coach. That is not to say that he actually kissed Tony Curtis himself.

"No, no, no. No. Don't misunderstand," he said. "Oh, no. You can coach a swimmer without getting in to the pool. You can teach somebody how to dive without getting wet."

So Cyril said he taught Tony Curtis how to kiss in the first place. And Tony Curtis went on to wonderful things and Cyril said he was the man who taught him how to do that. And now Cyril was home and retired and living on his earnings.

It seemed to locals who made these things their business that neither Frances nor Cyril were over-anxious to be in one another's company for all their Hollywood experiences.

But it came about at a Christmas party that they were thrown together for they found themselves as set dancing partners and swirling about the place when the music was high.

41

Frances allowed that she liked Cyril's company and that he was funny. And Cyril allowed that it was nice to meet somebody of his own experience and somebody, like himself, that had been at the heart of Hollywood. In the good days.

It was no surprise that after a whirlwind romance Frances and Cyril became engaged to be married and since there was no impediment that either would own up to and there didn't seem to be any other families left behind in America that they had been married to, the local priest agreed to marry them.

The entire town turned out. While it was unusual at the time for the priest to allow any sexual contact between married couples such as kissing in public in a church the priest was quite carried away with the thought that he had two surrogate stars on the altar.

Before him stood a woman who had kissed Rock Hudson and a man who had instructed a shy Tony Curtis in the art of kissing girls.

The priest said bravely, and everybody heard him, that Cyril could "kiss the bride." After both of them had said "I do."

And so Cyril turned to Frances on the altar and lifted her veil and he kissed her.

And it was a June wedding. Frances was not wearing her summer frock; she wore a bridal gown bought in a swop shop in the next town on a day's excursion in a taxi.

When Cyril kissed her she kissed him back and the entire congregation had a sense of déjà vu. For they had seen this scene many times in the cinema; but so too had Frances and so too had Cyril.

And when they kissed, it was obvious to the experienced kissers in the congregation --- and there were experienced kissers in the congregation --- that this was no Hollywood kiss.

This was the kiss of two people who had never been kissed before.

If anybody found anything amiss with the bride or the groom some of them said well perhaps you had to be there in Hollywood to know these things.

After all, in real life there is only one take.

In Hollywood there are many.

No Hatchet Man

It would be nice to think we are all honest in everything we do; but sadly, this is not always the case, as Danny discovered when his car was stolen in the weeks before Christmas.

He and Tanya owned two cars and parked them in the drive outside their new house. They were very proud of their new home, their togetherness and their new cars. They even took casual pictures with their Blackberry phones and sent them to their pals.

Danny mocked Tanya and her car to his pals and Tanya mocked Danny and his to her pals; but both of them were very proud and the future was bright.

One night, however, some thieves jacked up Tanya's car onto four concrete blocks in the driveway of her house, to steal her flashy alloy wheels, while she slept.

When they were done, they left Tanya's car where it was, wheelless. They then stole Danny's car to drive away in with Tanya's wheels in the boot.

Sort of a case of having five spare wheels.

The robbers were not content to steal a car --- and four good wheels --- but were intent on using Danny's car for a post office robbery later that day. They were resourceful robbers who liked to multi-task.

The plan was to use Danny's car as the safe car. They would rob the post office on a motor bike, stolen earlier, and drive to the parked stolen car to make off in it for an early Christmas celebration.

Matters do not always go to plan, and when Danny rang to report that not only were Tanya's wheels gone, but his car was stolen, he was told he had to report it in person in his local Garda station.

"How am I get to the Garda station?" he asked. "I have no car to get there."

He added that Tanya's car would not go far on four concrete blocks; but to no avail.

"That is the procedure," said the garda. "Could you not use a bus to travel to the station? We're open all hours. We never close. "

There was no bus route between him and the Garda station; so, Danny started to walk there, a journey of three miles.

It was no distance at all except the matter was of the gravest urgency for Danny who realised that until he got to the station and made the official report a nationwide search for his car could not swing into place.

During this time, nobody would be looking for his car as he had yet to officially report it missing; so he jogged a little and then broke into a run when he hoped nobody was watching him.

He ran down the middle of the road to see if he could travel faster there than he could travel on the path; but he was almost knocked down by a passing cement lorry. He hopped onto the path and began walking really fast, once more.

He began jogging again with his hand on his trousers pocket in case his mobile phone fell out and broke on the ground.

He needed the phone because Tanya needed to know where he was so that the comforting Lasagne she was preparing for both of them would be nice and ready when he returned home.

Danny slowed down to catch his breath as he passed by the local school and thought he was seeing things.

He re-traced his steps until he was approaching the school again, only this time at a slower pace, and from a different angle.

Sure enough, he was not seeing things. He had to ring Tanya straightaway and tell her. She couldn't believe it either. She said so. "I can't believe it," she said.

Danny's car was sitting outside the school as if its driver had returned to full-time education and was going to come back to the car as soon as lessons were over for the day.

When Danny tried the door it was open to his touch. He sat in and attempted to use his key to start it.

But the robbers had ripped the ignition from the steering column and the key was useless. He twiddled about with the wires to see if he could persuade the car to re-start but he was perplexed by the wires and colours that lay before him. Danny was not an engineer and getting the cap off a tamper-proof bottle sometimes proved a task too far for him.

He tucked the wires up as best he could and got back out to check the boot lid to see if it would open. This time, the key turned in the lock.

Danny was pleasantly surprised at what he found there. There they were sitting there looking up at him.

Tanya's four wheels, just as they had been taken from the car. And what was more --- and a bonus too --- the battery powered wheel brace the thieves had used to remove the wheels from Tanya's car was there as well.

Danny thought he would give himself a bonus and not report the finding of the wheel brace to the gardaí. He would keep it for himself and there it was.

Dishonest or not, he felt he and Tanya deserved a little bonus for what they had been through. He would tell the gardaí about the hatchet, though.

It was sitting in amongst the wheels where it should not be. Neither Danny nor Tanya owned a hatchet; they had no call for one in a new house that did not have a real fireplace or a real chimney that would burn real wood. So they did not to buy a hatchet in the DIY shop when they were choosing tools for their new home.

Danny was about to close the boot lid when he heard a motorbike approaching at speed and fearful of a collision stepped onto the path until the bike passed by.

It slowed to a halt and Danny distinctly heard the bike fall to the ground followed by some very strong swearing.

He stepped around to see if he could help somebody else, now that fortune had smiled on him what with recovering his car, Tanya's wheels, and a battery-powered wheel brace as well.

He was quite shocked to see the two riders jumping into his car to drive it away. Danny ran to the driver's door and pulled it open.

"That's my car," he said in a voice that was a pitch too high to be be forceful enough.

"We stole it first. If you want to rob a car you better go and get another one for yourself. This is ours," said the driver.

"It's my car. I paid road tax on it for a year. It's insured for both me and Tanya to drive," said Danny.

He said these things so the robber would know he was an honest man.

The robber got the car to start and pulled away. Just as he picked up the motorbike to give chase, a garda car came around the corner on foot of an earlier report of a man running down the middle of the road, interfering with traffic, and causing a danger.

Naturally enough, the two gardaí were pleased to catch what they believed to be a robber as he attempted to re-start the motor-bike that had been used in the post office robbery.

No amount of explaining by Danny would convince the gardaí that Danny was the innocent party. They insisted on taking him to the local station where he was held under suspicion; until Tanya arrived on a borrowed bicycle to identify him and to report the car and her four wheels stolen.

Excellent detective work saw Danny's car being recovered the next day from the canal. It had been submerged.

When it was pulled out, they discovered that Tanya's wheels were gone for good. But there was a bonus.

The thieves' wheelbrace was there and Danny by now quite cross with the robbers, said it was his all along. He claimed it.

The hatchet was nowhere to be seen and for that Danny was grateful. For whatever else he was, Danny was no hatchetman.

From then, up to Christmas and beyond, he used the wheelbrace to remove Tanya's replacement alloys at night.

They kept the wheels under the stairs every night until Tanya sold the car for a different colour, when Easter came.

Danny did not replace his car. He took up jogging and got a dog for security.

Next time he'd be ready for anything.

Dreaming a Miracle

Some people have dreams that please them and leave them in good form all day.

Others endure dreams that disturb and pervade the daylight hours.

Paul was prey to bad dreams.

He was a single man who was left his late parents' house as his home for life; as a consequence of being the youngest in the family.

A short while ago, Paul had a bad dream. He described it to Jesse the postman the next morning as a very disappointing dream.

"I dreamt I died of nothing. And it was all a waste," he told Jesse; who agreed it was a terrible thing before vaulting on to his postman's bike to pedal away a bit faster than usual, with his dog trotting after him.

Anybody that Paul told about the dream had the same reaction. If he was alive, then where was the problem?

It worried Paul that his death had been for nothing. He decided the best way to affirm life was to celebrate his non-death with his true friends.

He had no money; so the next best thing was to have a wake. For himself.

He called in to Alan's house to tell him he had some bad news. Alan sat him down and heard that Paul had been told he was dying and since no cause could be found for it, there would be no cure. Paul added, in the spirit of fair play, that it had been like a dream when he heard the news.

"I would like to gather my friends about me to say farewell; but I have no funds at the moment. I wonder if you might meet me for a last drink tomorrow night in any pub of your choosing," he proposed to Alan.

"Of course," Alan said. "I will, no question, and don't worry about paying for anything, I'll look after that."

Paul said thank you, and agreed a time and venue before hugging Alan and swearing him to confidentiality.

Alan agreed to such a sensitive request, for who wouldn't? Paul wanted to be remembered as he was, not as a suitable case for sympathy.

He invited another eleven people to make up a round dozen men at his wake. All were told privately and sworn to confidentiality as to the nightmare that Paul was living through.

Some accepted the first hug they'd had in years from him. All agreed to turn up with funds for a final drink.

When they did, they found a corner of the biggest pub in the town was requisitioned by Paul's disciples for a farewell worthy of a High King.

All knew why they were there; but none mentioned the true cause. For they were drinking men of discretion, to a man.

Paul gave them an alibi when he said it was his farewell to fond friends before he left on a journey.

So, they drank to that, and Paul sang a few verses of the Fields of Athenry, and the company joined in the chorus with doleful voices.

"Quit singing or leave," said the barman. "No singing here."

They repaired to Alan's house where he also lived alone, a consequence of his wife having moved in with the local carpenter after he came to fix a creaking door that Alan had neglected to do anything about.

Under the circumstances, Alan refused to pay him for the door. The carpenter insisted that his professional and emotional lives were two different parts of his being and he must be paid; but there the matter rested, for the moment; even though Paul had offered to go down and have a word with the carpenter and to bring Alan's wife back, as well. Paul said no.

The mourning party piled in to Alan's house and some even admired the work on the door, all things considered. The others sang the songs that Paul liked and admired.

Some slept, as the night wore on, and a few went to the filling station to get food for the company when morning was on the horizon.

The party staggered on for most of the day. The evening found them in a different pub once more drowning Pauls' sorrow.

All were set fair for another night and day in their unspoken grief when Sandra arrived in.

Sandra was one of Paul's fiancées and she was cross that she had not been included in the invitation to Paul's farewell party.

She particularly wanted to know where Paul was going, since this was the first she had heard of it. Paul calmed her down with an assurance that she would be told all about it, And, in private, once he had had a few drinks with the lads. Paul gave her a little hug that cheered her up.

Sandra accepted a drink or two and began to wonder what this trip was about and whether she might need to pack much. But then Martina arrived to ask what was going on, word having spread that Paul was leaving on a journey.

Martina was also Paul's fiancée though he had assured Sandra that it was all off, and he told Martina that he had no interest in Sandra, at all.

The row between the two women caused the party to be asked to leave the pub once more.

Some of the men were uncomfortable with the new situation, especially since it was obvious that neither woman was aware of the living nightmare Paul was going through. And that his friends were helping him face like a man.

Paul took the women to one side and spoke quietly to them. It was obvious, to those who study body language, that they were also shocked to receive the news. They even stopped arguing with one another for the time being.

After a shocked silence, all three had a group hug. Paul borrowed a mobile phone and ordered a taxi to come, immediately, to where they were. When the car arrived, Paul prevailed on both women to get in and go to his house and to wait for him there until he said goodbye to his pals.

When the weeping women were gone, Con, a friend from school-days asked: "Paul, have you considered a prayer at all?"

The others thought this couldn't hurt and they were led in prayer on the street by Con, having been evicted from the pub by the manager who refused to step to one side to be briefed privately by one of the party on exactly what was happening.

Paul was suitably emotional at the prayer meeting and tears flowed freely along their stubbled cheeks. He called for a second taxi.

While he waited, he said goodbye to all and thanked them for their friendship and prayer and said it made him feel better already.

Off he went in the taxi and the following morning he and his brace of fiancées repaired to a hotel and spa in a nearby town for a break, paid for by the grieving women.

Paul left them by the swimming pool after a few days and took a solitary bus to Mayo and Knock where he stayed for two more nights. He bought a few souvenirs before returning home, a happy man.

"I have been cured," he cried. "It's a miracle. Praise be. Thanks be to Con, for his intercession."

In fairness, he called to all of his disciples to share the good news and to thank them for their prayers and good wishes.

He said: "Boys. I'm cured."

He settled matters with Martina and Sandra when he said he was not yet ready for a long commitment and freed them to pursue other interests. Neither was happy; but both were content that the other woman did not get Paul, who was still free and could come back at any time, given a little encouragement.

Paul was much sought after for a while as a person who had experienced a miracle cure. The local paper rang up seeking an interview and his picture was on page seven on one of the weeks, as well as a few words on his new philosophy of life: "Live in the moment with your friends," said Paul to anybody that would listen.

After a while, his pals drifted away not quite sure whether they were glad or sorry that he had returned from the dead.

Not quite sure whether they had been taken for a ride, or not.

As for Paul, he changed bedrooms in his house and found that lying in the back bedroom was much quieter than in the master bedroom at the front where it was so noisy that it gave you bad dreams.

Dan the Moving Man

It's hard to believe now; but up to a few years ago lifts in office blocks and department stores were manned by a lift assistant who asked you politely where you wanted to go and then closed an outer door and an inner door and pressed the button for the appropriate floor.

Once there, both doors were opened by the same person who had travelled politely with you. You got out and went about your business, along with everybody else.

Then, as with many other things, people were replaced by automation and now we press buttons for ourselves and life is a little duller and lonelier as a result.

Lift people are no more as a profession, at least as far as we know.

Dan Mac was of the old school, who took little heed of advances in technology unless it affected his life directly. When he encountered an automated lift and an open-plan office for the first time more than a little confusion and mayhem ensued.

Dan is one of life's simpler souls who never managed to learn to read or write and who carried a firm belief within him that people were talking about him.

This caused confusion in the street when he stopped to ask strangers what they had just said --- about him. To which the answer most often was "what?" Because mostly the person hadn't noticed his approach.

Dan usually stared at the person and said: "Just watch it."

For his own amusement, he had a habit of sitting on a low wall in the town pretending not to notice an acquaintance as they passed by.

People were mostly happy he hadn't seen them and hurried on.

But they were called back by name in such a loud voice that everybody could hear the call. The only way to quieten him was to return to face him where he sat

He would ask: "Where would you be if I hadn't called you?"

To which the only answer was: "Further away from a fool than I am now."

At which Dan would rock back and forth at the good of it all, assured that people were talking about him, and this time to his face.

Such life skills as Dan possessed did not lead to much luck in the way of continuous employment, either, where people tended to avoid him, as much as possible.

He was inclined to pursue somebody for a job of his choosing, often with the intercession of somebody else desperate to see the back of him for a while.

Once hired Dan was satisfied of his worth and abandoned the job.

Many employers sent him out on messages only to find he never returned or misunderstood the instruction.

Sam Magee, a local accountant, who hired him as a general go-fer for a while, handed him a tenner one day and asked him to go down to the shops and change it for ten singles.

Sam of course meant ten units of currency, since he wanted to place one in each of ten envelopes for an experiment he wanted to conduct with a new recruit.

After some time passed and Dan was still missing, Sam wrote off the tenner and resolved not to hire anybody else for a while at least not from the ranks of the daft.

Dan came back, several hours later, and walked into Sam's inner office where Sam was conferring with his wealthiest client on tax avoidance measures and placed a large paper bag on the desk.

"They weren't open when I got there, I had to wait," said Dan with the air of an explorer newly arrived home from a hazardous journey.

Wisps of steam rose up from the brown paper bag. Dan seemed to expect praise, if not outright applause.

"Who wasn't open?" asked Sam Magee.

Dan looked from one to the other as if it were the silliest question he had heard in a good while.

"The chipper," he said: "Didn't you ask for ten singles? I got salt in a separate bag; they had no sauce until tonight."

The immediate loss of that job was one of life's profound mysteries, as far as Dan was concerned.

He was asked to do something and he did so, and got a twist of salt while he was at it and was sacked on the spot.

So when Willie the carpenter called to his house to ask if he wanted to come with him in the van for the day he agreed to go. At least Willie knew what he wanted.

Willie paid cash and all he asked was that Dan hold the end of an office desk or something else he was delivering to one of the new offices.

As they drove along Dan told Willie what happened with the accountant and Willie agreed that Dan was correct in his belief that people in offices had no sense whatsoever.

Once arrived at the delivery point, Willie told Dan to remain in the van to protect the desk against hijackers. When he heard Dan shouting at a passing cyclist to "mind his own business" he hurried into the building and up to the fourth floor to where the desk was consigned.

The lift doors opened directly onto an open plan office that filled the full floor.

A reception area was stationed opposite the main lift and the adjacent fire escape stairs. The receptionist could see who was coming or going and respond accordingly.

Willie established that he was on the correct floor and found where the desk was to be placed and went off to fetch it and its minder.

Dan was by now standing in the street smoking a Woodbine, without a care in the world.

They manoeuvred the desk into the lift and Willie was happy they had not had to use the stairs to get to the fourth floor with their delivery. Dan was not a man to avoid corners and he had to be watched lest he knock lumps out of the building with the wooden desk on the way. Not to mention wrecking the desk as well.

Willie always made a point of handing Dan the delivery docket to have it signed when they made a delivery. It was a gentle tribute to Dan and recognition that he had assisted in the undertaking.

It usually went well, with Dan always checking the signature to see that it was where it should be on the sheet even though he could not read and off they'd go.

This time, on arrival in the lift on floor four Dan presented the docket to the receptionist who, having been primed on Dan's background by Willie, nodded and told Dan where the desk was to go.

However, this meant that when Dan turned back to Willie and the desk, Dan was on the outside of the lift. He had not noticed that Willie was holding his hand over the electronic eye that closed the doors automatically, when all was clear.

The doors remained open as long as Dan braced himself in the doorway and blocked the electronic beam.

Once he straightened up with his end of the burden he was no longer in line with the beam and the doors closed behind him with both him and Willie and the desk inside a closed lift, once more.

Willie showed him which button to press to open the lift and they tried again --- with the same results.

When the lift closed a third time, this time caressing Dan's buttocks in passing, he decided the receptionist was playing tricks and pressing a button at her desk to close the doors when he wasn't watching.

He shouted "Hey you…" at the startled woman before Willie grabbed him and restrained him from advancing on her position.

Willie directed Dan to the inside of the lift and made sure his own leg blocked the beam, until they were safely out of the elevator.

When the desk was safely dropped into place, Willie caught Dan once more to ask where the docket had gone.

When he heard the receptionist had it and that Dan was going back to sort her out, Willie now told a lie.

"We're in the wrong building, Danny. I've only realised it now," said Willie. "I tell you what. Let's leave the desk here, I'll get the woman to sign for it and we'll scarper down the stairs."

Scarper was a word that Dan liked. They would scarper and leave these fools to move the desk themselves.

But he couldn't resist a parting shot at the receptionist as they left the floor: "We're off for chips; and if anybody wants change of a tenner they can go themselves."

Willie told Cathy the receptionist that Dan was a little soft and did she fancy a drink later on?

But Cathy walked away without answer and when Willie saw a security man approaching the reception area he too scarpered.

On the way down the stone stairs he could hear the echoes of Dan shouting back up so to hear the echo of his own voice.

"Fooled yiz..."

Maybe Dan was right: a good bag of chips and a smoke would see things right.

Anyway, people in offices know nothing anyway.

That's a fact.

High Flying Annie

Annie slept in a bedroom that faced south. She liked it when the sun shone in her bedroom in the evening. She often sat there to draw peace and contentment from the yellow light. It was like being in Florida before a hurricane came, she said, nice and quiet and warm even if there was a breeze on the way.

The heat and sun that visited that room for the longest period was the main reason her son Eddie grew cannabis in her bedroom.

He planted it in earthen flower pots and placed a row of them in a line on the floor opposite the window in the small room, where the sun reached first and for the longest time. Then he went home to his own house.

When one or the other needed a boost he placed it on the windowsill for direct sunlight, so it would come on a little faster.

That the house faced onto the street and had a short garden meant that anybody walking past could look up and see the pots in the window.

Annie was of the generation that liked to see neat white lace curtains on a window; but Eddie felt that to get the full effects of the sun on the cannabis it needed to stand in front of the curtain. So when he called to visit his parents, Annie and Danny, he always moved the pots in front of the curtain. And when he was gone, Annie always slipped the curtain back in front of the plant.

As for Danny, he neither knew nor cared what was going on. Danny had entered the early world of dementia a while back and was confined to what had been the master bedroom of the house. He slipped in and out of the moment as his condition dictated.

Annie left their bed when he asked her one night who she was and what would happen to her if his wife returned early from bingo and found her in Annie's bed?

He said: "It's all the same to me where you sleep, for you're a fine looking woman; but there can be no talk of any shenanigans because I'm a married man and that's that."

So, Annie claimed the small bedroom for her new resting place.

Danny didn't seem to notice; but Annie had to answer his questions about the lodger that had come to live in the house.

"She's a good looking girl; but a bit forward and she needs to be watched. She's a farmer's daughter," he said. "I know because she's started to plant things around the house. And she is a bit free with where she sleeps."

Annie told Eddie while Eddie picked some of the leaves for cooking in the kitchen cooker. But Eddie said not to mind his father, for nobody would believe anything he said. He was mad, was Eddie's final verdict on the man that had created him.

Once more, Annie said she was a little nervous that Eddie was growing an illegal substance in the bedroom. But Eddie said it was easier than handing money over to drug dealers who in Eddie's opinion were the dregs of the earth.

In a former life they would have been grave robbers; now they just robbed lives, for money.

Eddie on the other hand, liked a smoke, so his compromise was that he would grow his own.

It was hard for Annie to argue with that, and anyway, when she was a young woman moving in a long flowing dress in the long meadows of a summer morning she had smoked her own with her handsome lover Danny.

But she never told Eddie that. Sometimes, a parent doesn't share everything with a child, even an only child as Eddie was.

Neither did Eddie share much with her.

Eddie's girlfriend of the past year was giving him some grief, Eddie explained to Annie on a fine Tuesday morning when he was rotating his crop in the bedroom and tending to the oven as a conscientious potsmoker.

Since he rarely gave her any indication of how his life with Giselle was proceeding Annie knew matters were on a perilous footing.

When his mobile phone rang in the middle of the conversation Eddie listened intently without speaking and Annie knew from her only son's look that something was happening.

He hung up and said: "I have to go to Galway."

Then he was gone, heading off to intercept the Galway to Dublin bus in an attempt to catch up with the departed Giselle.

Annie found this out later when Eddie wrote to tell her what had happened after Danny appeared in court accused of being in possession of drugs for supply to others.

But that was later.

Annie blamed herself for smoking the joint that Eddie left behind in his rush to catch the passing bus. It was there, as were several others that she smoked later while sh ewas at it. It was like she had gone back in time after the first draw.

She felt nice. So nice that she went and found a longish dress to wear. She walked to the meadows for a think about lots of things.

And to see the colours.

But there were houses in the meadow now and the people that owned the mortgages on the houses had surrounded bits of the meadow with walls and called them their gardens.

So Annie went down to the river and sat on the bank to see if she could see the multicoloured fish again. She had been away for a while; but she was back now. She told the fish that; but none of them answered her; so she waited.

Back at the houseDanny was being arrested by the gardaí for conduct likely to lead to a breach of the peace.

When he found the house empty , after his nap, he called for Annie but Annie was no longer there. So he decided she had been kidnapped. A state of affairs that made sense only to Danny. But he acted on it, nonetheless, and went looking for the farmer's daughter that had taken Annie away from him

While he was at it, he threw out all the pots of plants that he had seen her growing things in. They landed in the front garden and spilled their contents on the ground.

Neighbours tried to calm Danny down; but he was untouchable.

In his mind he was back in his days of most agility and strength and was fighting fit. He could take anybody on.

The gardaí needed four strong men to hold him down and to take him to the station. They called in drug detectives when they saw the pot plants scattered around the garden.

More stuff was found in the house and since Danny was the registered houseowner, he was responsible.

He tried to tell them that it was the farmer's daughter that did it; but it was no use.

He had to be charged, there was just too much cannabis in the house for one man.

Anyway, since Danny had stopped making real sense to anybody except Eddie and Annie it was hard for the gardaí not to assume he was on his own drugs; so they locked Danny up, pending a court appearance.

An oblivious Annie remained on the bank of the river waiting for the petals to come by in a phantasmagory of colour when they dipped over the white weir.

Giselle went to Shannon and boarded a plane and flew away. She only told Eddie she was for Galway because she knew he would follow her there and she was sick of him and his mad plants.

Eddie wandered the streets of Galway asking people if they had seen Giselle? But nobody had so he came home to a wrecked house and a trampled front garden.

All he had done was to go to Galway after Giselle and now he had lost his girl, his mother and his father. Though when he heard what happened to Danny, Eddie went to the garda station and told them the cannabis plants were his.

The gardaí said they had to charge somebody and they already had the houseowner in custody.

Danny claimed the drugs belonged to a woman he described as a farmer's daughter. Did Eddie know who she was, by any chance?

Eddie had to say he did not; but added that his dad was a little confused lately and might be mixed up.

It was no use, the garda said; Eddie could appear in court and take his chances with his father in the dock, if he wished; but Danny was getting charged and that was that, said the garda.

Annie came home from the river but left straight away for Scotland and an island community there. On the way, she bought a guitar at a furniture auction and a songbook in a tourist shop.

She was going to write poetry and songs and be Annie Slow Hand once more.

Danny was declared unfit to plead when he asked the judge if he wanted to arm wrestle him and was hospitalised for his own good.

He still looked for Annie.

If he found the farmer's daughter he would ring her neck, he said, and people smiled at the silliness of it all.

For there's nothing sillier than a family gone to pot.

Eddie went to live in Galway in case Giselle ever came looking for him.

Private Writer

There was a man who lived in the town, whose name was Joe, who was married to a woman who was a gifted writer --- though she never received recognition at least not until Joe was killed one dark night.

Mary ran a discreet service for married couples, especially those couples where one or the other was serving overseas in the armed forces on peacekeeping missions.

She wrote love letters for wives too tongue-tied to write for themselves.

Joe took up writing responses for husbands. Sadly, he was taken away as he was coming down Tinker's Hill one dark night on a bike with no lights on it and what turned out to be faulty breaks.

He only found out about the brakes when he failed to stop before he met an oncoming truck and was transported unwillingly a distance back up the hill on his way to a large funeral.

This was writ large in the farewell messages read in the graveyard.

Mary mourned Joe's passing. But try as she might; she could not suppress a smile at his transition from cycling husband to saint in heaven.

Joe was an avid follower of the Tour de France on television and fancied himself a contender had he been born in different circumstances, and had a chance to practice. That and a decent bike.

As it was in his spare time he trained young cyclists by driving in his car behind them smoking cigarettes while he concentrated on the training schedule of his charges.

His death bike was a rogue bike he had been working on to make it go faster. He was testing it and the law of gravity on the steep hill when the experiment ended.

His death gave Mary an opportunity to write to mourners to thank them for their concerns. It also gave her the opportunity to showcase her writing business a little more without being too obvious about it.

She had written discreet love letters from their wives to men; but what the women did not know was that she also replied to them.

The men, for the most part, were pleased at their wives' words of love and flew off happily to wherever the jaws of danger awaited.

Each was sworn not to open the letter until airborne when it was too late to wonder at the pen that constructed the letter. Mary always insisted that the client re-write the letter in their own handwriting for the sake of confidentiality.

This service discreet as Mary was tended to be hinted at by some wives in a somewhat half-hearted attempt to convince their returned husbands of their fidelity, since last they met.

Did they not send the best love letters they ever read? And why should the temporarily-absent one be concerned at false reports of homeland infidelity?

It was all the gossip of people jealous of the wonderful life they had together.

It was only a matter of time before husbands asked Joe whether he could provide the male equivalent and how much would that be?

For men are not always fools.

Joe declared he could certainly do so, given a few days' notice.

He went to Mary and suggested she write for the other side of the house as well and he would write the letters out in his own hand, so that nobody would be any the wiser.

Double money.

Soon enough, there was a small industry going on in the Joseph and Mary household.

On some days Mary wondered if she were going quietly mad herself at the complexity of it all, for she was privy to secrets she would rather not know about, at times.

Since Mary wrote both male and female letters, there was a time when she was indeed writing to herself for she was often supplying letters to both sides of the divide, in times of stress.

Mary saved more marriages through her writing than prayers for intercession at the Marian shrine at Knock ever did.

Joe for his part took to the writing business like a lark to the skies.

He even began writing short stories and showing them to the men who called for their letters of commitment which they supposed were penned by Joe.

Most men told Joe that he was good at the stories and wished him well they having more things on their minds than made up stories.

Securing the home against boarders while they were away being the chief concern amongst many of them.

Joe agreed with some offhand remarks made by departing husbands that his writing should be published in a book. He often said he was in talks with somebody about it; but he was only talking to himself; for he was lifting yarns from story collections and re-writing them as his own.

He would take a story set in Japan and re-locate it to downtown Lucan with appropriate name changes; he would borrow a story set in the American west and set it in the west of Ireland. A big city story set in New York worked just as well in a Dublin setting, Joe found.

All of this was harmless enough and went no further than Joe and a few pals until he and his bike were recycled on Tinker's Hill, without warning.

Some months later when she was trying to find some part of Joe left untouched in their home, Mary found his handwritten stories in an old document holder, and so began a new chapter in her writing life.

Mary was a very busy writer and was unaware of Joe's tomfoolery in re-writing other people's work. She not surprisingly took the handwritten stories for his own composition.

Some of them were even quite good, she thought, as she deciphered the handwriting and read through the many corrections and changes of locale that Joe had inked in from his original story.

In fact, when Joe absented himself from Mary of an evening for a stint in the box room, he often declared he was off for a little R'n R.

He meant read and re-write.

Mary thought he meant rest and relax while she battled to save marriages.

So moved was Mary that she set up a self publishing house in the kitchen of their home and published Joe's work in booklet format.

It went well and lots of people bought copies and sent them off to friends and relations living abroad, as a memento of the good old days around the town.

So well did it go, with local media attention, that Mary was considering writing several more books in Joe's voice and passing them off as newly discovered manuscripts, so as to create a legend.

She would say she discovered them in the attic.

That is until the postman delivered several official looking letters one Friday morning pointing out that the real writers of the posthumously published lifts were seeking redress and retraction.

Mary now realised that Joe led a double life as a stealer of other people's words. She closed down the imprint and went back to writing letters for the female side of her clientele.

Mary's heart was in her boots and she could not whip up sufficient enthusiasm for male letters. She no longer trusted the male voice.

Though that didn't stop her, every Valentine's Day, from writing love letters to selected women she felt were in need of an anonymous lover.

Mary wrote like a man and sent messages to those who could handle such declarations without becoming deranged.

And if it added to the gaiety of lives, who could fault her for that? Mary liked to keep her customers satisfied.

She believed strongly in giving back to her community, so whenever anybody was not happy, she wrote a happy letter for them.

Whenever a man or a woman was doing wrong by their partner, Mary sent a warning note to them.

All done anonymously, of course.

Everybody knew that it was Mary that was doing it; but nobody would say so.

For that would be the end of the game, and without Mary and her words there would be no game in town.

Lash Larrie

Since somebody passed a law banning the wandering abroad of dogs without human supervision the streets and roads of Ireland have lost a lot of their character and excitement.

It used to be the case that almost every house had a dog of its own or a dog claimed ownership of a family for as long as he cared to stay there.

Some dogs strayed, some for a few hours in pursuit of a female in heat; or for a few days if there was no excitement to be had locally and a sensible dog had to travel for diversion.

Some left home and never came back. They just took up residence in another place as a stray. It was an easy thing to accomplish since dogs do not speak a language known to humans and could not be quizzed on their origins or home address.

This led to various disputes amongst dogs on which home it was best for a single dog to take up lodgings in. And dog fights often occurred.

A defeated dog could become vicious and even a winning dog could become cross with all the scrapping he did to preserve his space.

A vicious dog was generally allowed to bite as many other animals as he wished without penalty; but when it came to human beings it was a different matter altogether.

A dog that bit a man was under a suspended sentence of death. Three bites and he was out of this world for good. If he attacked sheep there was no question of due process; the shepherd just shot the dog down and that was that.

So, when a favourite dog started to become vicious, a caring owner might look for a safe home for the dog; so that it could live a little longer.

Tom was a man who owned a former farmhouse on a road that was quiet for years but suddenly became busy following the appearance of new housing estates in the green fields nearby.

He liked dogs and he very rarely refused lodging to a dog that was vicious.

The result was that he had quite a few curs of various tempers, hue and ancestry about the place.

Nobody ever bothered to break in on the premise that they would be chewed to death by the dogs, once inside.

Tom kept them in line with his voice. Legitimate callers were not bothered by the pack so long as a member of the family first introduced them to the dogs.

He generally welcomed a new addition with a few calm words of reassuarance and left the dog to settle in with the others. If the newcomer became obstreperous and started to bite out of place, Tom simply punched the animal in the jaw, like John Wayne punching a horse into submission. He only ever did this once since most dogs were so shocked at the blow that they toed the line and peace reigned once more.

Then a law was passed that dogs had to be kept under control, be tagged, licensed and civilised. The result was that few animals wandered the streets alone in search of canine craic, anymore.

Dog pounds were set up and bureaucracy swung into action. It was decreed that anybody that had a dog was to have a licence to keep the dog; which had always been the case; but the new regulations meant that dog inspectors fanned out seeking unlicensed animals and revenue from new licence payers.

In one large local housing estate two inspectors arrived to seek stray animals to impound or to insist that the licence fee be paid on their behalf --- dogs having no disposable income to meet the bill.

They found dogs' homes by walking around back lanes and knocking on the back gates whereupon the dog in domicile would launch himself at the gate to protect its territory.

There was little an owner could say in contradiction of the inspector's claim that a dog resided there and should have a licence, when the dog in question was taking bites out of the back wall.

So, bit by bit and little by little the interesting dog population gave way to pampered pets paraded on a leash by their concerned owners, many of whom carried insurance in case the moggy needed specialist treatment.

All of which was good news to Larry who cycled some miles to work each morning and cycled the same some miles back in the evening.

Each time he passed a country house with a dog in residence, the mongrel would take off after Larry and his bike in a game attempt to devour Larry, the bike, or at least a wheel.

That they did not succeed was due to Larry's turn of speed on the bike. But Larry was growing older and growing more and more fed up with the daily dog chase.

Tom's house and grounds were a particular problem whenever the pack of recovering street fighting dogs escaped their bounds. Larry resembled nothing more than a hunt in full flight with the cursing cyclist as the quarry when that happened.

Long before the new houses grew in the fields nearby the South Dublin Hunt used to chase across the hinterland of Lucan.

Larry was often glad when he had to work on Saturdays to see the hunt coming through the fields because it distracted Tom's pack of animals who were never quite sure what to make of it all. So many horses, so many hounds. Outnumbered and surrounded.

Sometimes, the hunt attracted protestors who complained about it all and then went home for a bowl of soup to warm up.

It happened on one Monday following a hunt that Larry spotted a whip lying in a ditch. It was there in full view. He looked around cautiously to see if anybody else was about before he picked it up.

Whether it was a whip that belonged to the hunt, or to a protestor or somebody else entirely was of no interest to Tom because he had a new use for it.

He brought it home and out into the back garden where he spent a long evening practicing the correct method of clipping leaves off a tree with the tip of the lash.

The next day Larry set off to work on the bike as usual and when he came to Tom's place he rang the bell on the handlebar of the bike to attract the dogs out after him.

He would have it out, now or never.

The unsuspecting pack tumbled out to wreak havoc on Larry and the bike only to be met by a strange cracking sound as Larry sat high in the saddle and cracked the whip like any good master of hounds might do.

As with all things new, Larry took the matter a stage further. He was not happy to confuse the dogs with the cracking whip; but he whipped the end ever closer to the cross-bred alsation that gave him the most trouble.

Things would have been fine if the dog had not been boneheaded enough to keep coming at Larry and the bicycle. The road was potted and rutted and since Larry was a fairly new whipmaster he was not as accurate as he liked to think he was.

Catastrophically, the tail end of the whip wrapped itself around the alsation's testicles. The ensuing scream from the dog frightened even Larry.

He was even more frightened when the wounded animal took off with the lash wrapped around him and Larry on the other end of it holding on in panic; knowing that the pursuing pack would make mincemeat of him if it caught up with them.

The dogs did not know why the alsation was now ahead of the cyclist when the object was to devour the rider. But they kept on, anyway, to see what would happen.

The chase ended when the lash unwound and the dog went racing in through the next open field gate, followed by his confused pals.

Larry kept going as fast as he could. He avoided that road for a few days afterwards in case of repercussions.

But a reputation grew up around Larry in the town in the weeks that followed.

He confided in just one person in work, a fellow cyclist, who confided in just one other person and soon the whole population of the Earth knew what had happened, one at a time.

But the story grew until it was established --- on no basis of truth whatsoever --- that Larry could emasculate a racing Alsation without dismounting from his bicycle or even changing gear.

For a long time, Larry became known as Lash Larree, after a comic cowboy called Lash La Rue who existed in olden times, in boys' heads.

Then, he became known to his friends, and others, as Lash.

As for the alsation, who never had any offspring after that, nobody knows what he thought of the mad cyclist with the ball-teasing whip. Dogs are unable to speak a language that humans can understand, so he told nobody

But he stopped biting cyclists, or even chasing them and for Larry that was a blessing.

For his part, Tom renewed his shotgun licence and kept a few shells near the back door, just in case there was any more messing on the road.

Lash Laree or no Lash Laree; nobody was going to mess with his dogs who all deserved a quiet life and protection form a madman who thought that when he was on his bike he was master of Tom's hounds.

Bonny Smoking

Bonny is a woman who likes a smoke. She has smoked since she was a pre-teen, though the term wasn't invented then. People of that age were just called kids. And the description stuck until they went to work.

Bonny used to buy cigarettes, one at a time, in the local shop and ask for the loan of a match, when the shopkeeper was in a good mood.

If he was in bad form and said no, then she would ask for a light off the first person she met on the street.

Everybody smoked in those happy days when there were no smoke police to be found within an ash's flick of decent people. Bonny often said so to her Martin when he was in the mood for listening: "You could ask for a light and get one, no questions asked," she said.

People couldn't afford a lighter then; the price was too much of an investment when funds were tight.

"If I could afford a lighter, I could afford ten smokes at a time," Bonny explained patiently to the man that was trying to sell her a three-pack of shiny lighters, each one a different colour.

She was so short of money that sometimes, when she thought nobody was watching, she picked up discarded butts off the street and broke them open to get the tobacco out to roll them in her own cigarette paper.

But, then she moved on in the job and found that she could afford not only ten smokes at a time; but she could also buy a full box of matches for her own use.

She even offered a light to other smokers in the cinema when she finally purchased a Bic lighter of her own.

Martin worked in the same factory as she did, only in a different part. She didn't see him everyday or anything like that. At breaks the men sat with the men and the women sat with the women

The only connection was in the mutual slagging the groups gave one another, as part of the day.

In the cinema, Martin sat with the lads in their row and Bonny sat in her row.

Bit by bit, though, Martin found his way out to the edge of his row and Bonny did the same on her side so that after a while only the aisle separated them.

Casual looks were exchanged with increased frequency and Sally liked the way Martin's father cut his hair each week at home.

So, when Martin asked her what she thought of the picture coming up on Friday, Bonny naturally said it looked very good --- judging by the trailer they saw last week and the big coloured poster on the wall near the cinema.

Martin asked her who was in the picture on the day they were standing looking up at notices of the coming attractions. They had managed to be both looking up at the posters on this day when nobody else was around.

It might have seemed a coincidence to a casual observer; but Bonny hung around the poster wall for days at the same time, because she knew Martin liked to stand there when the new posters went up.

He asked anyone who came along what they thought of the picture that had been newly plastered on the high boards.

Each time, he asked a different person; each time he asked them who was in it, though their names were there to be seen.

That way, Martin could get by without anybody realising that he couldn't read or write.

But Bonny knew and always managed to read stuff out loud ahead of Martin having to ask anybody else.

Otherwise, Martin got his news from the radio and the local gossip in the job. He liked to back a horse and managed to get somebody to share the bet and write the docket for both of them.

Bonny said she would like to see the picture on Friday and Martin said he would too and Bonny waited and waited and then she said: "Maybe we might go together."

"Sit together?" said Martin. As if it was a big decision.

"Yes," said Bonny firmly.

Martin said "Right" in the manner of somebody who had made a life-changing decision.

They went to the pictures and Bonny insisted on paying for herself. Martin bought a pack of 20 cigarettes, tipped, king sized, and shared them with Bonny.

They sat inside a small fog of drifting smoke as the picture ran on the screen before them. Neither was able to say for sure afterwards what it had been about, who was in it, or how it ended.

Martin offered Bonny another cigarette: she said thanks; though her throat was so parched she could have given a smoked cod a swim for its money.

She could taste nothing but nicotine and cigarettes for days afterwards; but Bonny didn't care; she was officially in love.

She said his name to herself on the bike on the way into work on Monday morning, over and over.

Even when the slagging started and the women called her Martin for the whole morning, she managed to not blush all that much.

When she heard that Martin was in a fight with another man after the man called him Bonny all morning, she knew that she and Martin were set fair for the long haul.

They walked out and got engaged and married and found a labourer's cottage to live in for a while until the council gave them a house when they had enough kids to qualify for a council house.

By then, Bonny was no longer formally working and Martin was the main breadwinner.

Ends didn't always meet. So they did what ever was necessary to get by.

When things got bad, Martin used a credit account in the local shops to create some cash. He went from one to the other on Thursdays, the day before payday, and asked for five packets of cigarettes in each, on tick.

Then he went into the local pubs and sold the cigarettes to drinkers for half price, claiming quietly that they were off the back of a lorry.

Martin no longer smoked; but Bonny liked a fag every so often --- to keep her sane --- and Martin kept a 20-pack for her from the haul around the shops. But pyramid schemes all end some day.

Shop credit was cut off when the bills went unpaid for too long and since the factory had closed down years earlier and Martin was unemployed for so long, nobody called him for work anymore.

So Martin became a thief.

Just a little at first; he knew a house where the people were out all day and he knew how to get in the back door quietly. So, he went inside and for a while gently opened drawers and lifted clothes until he found their tea-caddy fund.

He told Bonny that a horse he backed with a pal had been the first of a series of lucky bets and the tide had turned and he was making a comeback and all would be well.

Bonny knew her man was lying but she said yes, it will turn: she knew it would.

He went on for a while like that and each time he took only cash. He still couldn't read and he was afraid of credit cards and what they said about somebody else.

Jewellery he left where he found it for it could be traced.

But fingerprints can be read and Martin neglected to wear gloves and the gardaí found fingerprints in a few houses. They eventually caught him coming out the back of a quiet house and it was only a matter of how long he would be put away for.

Bonny is a woman that likes a smoke.

She has smoked since she was a kid.

Bonny still smokes of an evening, only now she watches the pictures in her own house on her own on television while she waits for Martin to come home.

Her kids are grown and gone and Sarah, the eldest, goes to visit her father in prison and calls in to Bonny on Friday nights with enough cigarettes to get her through next week.

Bonny doesn't go to visit Martin.

She says she will wait until he comes home.

And then she will make up her mind what to do about his dishonesty.

Peter Petrol

In an age when cars are two a penny it can be hard to remember that not so long ago people bought petrol in milk bottles which while quite illegal and downright dangerous was the only way some young drivers could afford to buy fuel for their brand new second-hand car.

It's one of the reasons you see little signs on petrol pumps telling you what the minimum is that you may purchase at any time. This sometimes gives pause to buyers of lawnmower petrol when they try to estimate just what volume of petrol the machine needs to swallow to function. This is not as easy as it seems, for few people bother to read labels. Some will buy enough petrol for a small war while others will try to make do with so little that the poor lawnmower must exist on fumes.

The restriction was not put there to vex people; it was a campaign against the milk bottle buyer of petrol that survived the reason for its introduction.

At that time, most people drove onto a garage forecourt to purchase fuel. Petrol was filled by a young boy or an older man; neither of whom got much in the way of wages.

Most times, drivers went into the cash office and paid the cashier for the petrol bought and they might purchase a pint of oil for whenever the car's engine got too noisy for want of lubrication.

There wasn't much else to be bought in the garage. It was then a place you went to for attention to your car, not to your credit card.

If you told somebody you had bought a panini in the garage, and paid for it with a plastic card, you'd find yourself joining the happy, if confused, folk in dressing gowns and slippers in St Loman's hospital.

Peter, on the other hand, was a young man who was never confused at all. He knew what he wanted; but knew he had no money to buy what he sought.

To earn a few bob for his leisure pursuits, Peter worked on Main Street driving a taxi for the local cycle and radio shop of Joe Dignam which also sold bottled gas and Super Sers and fixed things when they broke down.

The business had a number of large black taxis that were more often seen in American gangster pictures, than on local roads. The cars had running boards that you could stand on while chatting to the driver as the car travelled along on a summer's day. They were employed to ferry Lucan people to and fro, since few people owned their own car, and were used anytime there was a local pilgrimage to Knock shrine in Mayo, for instance.

They didn't drive to Mayo however. They drove the pilgrims from the village to the railway station at Adamstown, where a passing train stopped to carry the pious and the sinner away for a day's praying in the rain.

Trains came back in the evening and everybody retired to bed happy with the excursion, if not with the high price of a cup of watery tea on the train.

Peter was a happy and convivial driver and people liked to travel in his car. He made a bit extra pennies in tips from his fares. It amounted to enough over time that he could pay a deposit on a very dilapidated car.

Few others of his age had a car and so it was a babe magnet in the days before such a term was heard in polite company.

In the excitement of it all, Peter's head was turned by a young woman whose family migrated from Lucan to Castleknock because Paula's father took a job there which included tenancy of a small cottage, which was his while he stayed alive and working in the job.

Peter was glad he had agreed to hire purchase the car. Though whether the car or the term of the purchase expired first was anybody's guess.

It meant he could still see Paula and could leave his girlfriend home to her house in his car, after a date.

But, the sad fact was that he couldn't afford to pay for the car, run it, and date a popular young woman at the same time.

So, to cope with fuel costs, he put aside a number of glass milk bottles for the purchase of a bare minimum of petrol for driving up hills and along flat stretches of roads.

His system was to park around the corner from the garage and walk in to the cash office. He explained that he had just run out of petrol, had no petrol can to carry the petrol to the car and had borrowed a pair of milk bottles to purchase a quart of petrol.

This was at a time when litres were something only continentals were intimate with.

A quart, as everybody knows, is one quarter of a gallon of petrol, the measure in use at the time. It equates to 1.136 litres according to a reliable page-a-day diary that gives this class of information at the turn of a page. And if more lawnmower buyers looked up such sources of information, much torment would be avoided on grass cutting weekends when the machine runs dry.

Peter would say to the cashier, with as sincere a face as he could muster, that he would return forthwith with the car and would fill up as soon as he got her started again with the two pints of petrol.

Of course, he did not return and would avoid that garage for a good while until he considered they'd forgotten his time-wasting purchases.

To save petrol Peter devised a system of driving along as fast as was safe --- and since there were few cars on the roads after dark, --- this was as fast as he could manage.

When the car was humming along and the ground was declining in front of him, he quietly turned the engine off and coasted along.

It was a system he devised from his cycling days when he pedalled hard and free-wheeled down the hill before him.

Many was the cyclist he passed on his descent to the bottom in the hurtling car who finished up off the road in shock at seeing a driver-less car pass them by at speed with no engine running.

Peter had reasoned it would be better for him to hunker down in the seat in case he was spotted by a patrolling Garda. He steered by looking through the steering wheel rather than by sitting over it. It gave a driver-less impression to terrified passers-by.

The car would reach the bottom of the hill and keep going as long as there was momentum. Just as it was about to expire Peter would drop it into gear jump-start the engine and drive on home in peace.

It all almost came to a tragic end when Peter was approached by a bunch of Chapelizod men seeking a lift from Castleknock to Chapelizod.

While it was out of his way, Peter estimated that a car switched off at Castleknock College crossroads would coast all the way to Chapelizod of its own volition, with no cost in fuel.

And since the Chapelizod men had agreed to throw in a few coins for fuel on Peter's journey back through Palmerstown and on to Lucan, Peter further estimated that if he switched off around Ballyowen Hill he might make Lucan, with cash to spare.

As many men piled in as the closing of both doors would allow. Some sat on laps. All went well until they reached the steep hill on the descent to Chapelizod village. There is a particularly vicious bend about half way down and as the turn approached out of the night Peter discussed with his passengers how he could drive without engine power and how the power of velocity was not to be discounted. He switched off the engine.

He made the mistake of taking the key from the ignition to wave it in the air to emphasise his point.

It was around the time that the then-new system of steering wheel lock came into play.

The lock on this car worked instantly and the car, with its occupants, continued in a straight line towards the high wall accompanied by masculine screams from the passengers.

That Peter got the key back into the ignition, broke the lock and scraped the car along the side of the wall is a testament to the power of prayer, and the positive effect of the full lungs of the passengers on Peter's eardrums.

Silence reigned in the car on the run in to the village.

Nobody spoke when they tumbled out onto the road when the car came to an eventual halt in the village square, outside the coalman's house.

None of them referred to screams in the car ever afterwards, though the story and the danger grew larger as the near-death experience faded away.

There were more prayers said in a shorter time on that descent than were said all the way to Knock by any number of pilgrims from Adamstown.

It proved what Peter always believed. You should never underestimate the power of prayer; especially if you're broke.

Tunnel of Love

Some men like to play with toys. Some fool around long after their childhood itself has chugged into dim memory.

Most manage to cloak their continuing interest by adapting grand titles for themselves. After all, it is a strange sight to see men play marbles in the open at the height of a summer's day.

But let them form a society of marble collectors and present an exhibition of traditional marble rolling in short trousers and there's a fair chance they could put in for a tourism grant and be successful.

Many will acknowledge openly that they like to continue to enjoy the things of childhood; even if it extends to laying out the back garden with an all-weather model train system that meanders around the lawn and through the shrubbery.

Some even wear a station master's hat to whistle down the tiny train as it passes their feet.

Gulliver never stopped travelling in some gardens of the mind.

Ned, for instance, was fond of gazing down from his back bedroom window at his neighbour's back garden and at the train set chugging past the red windmill in the other garden.

But he was very careful not to let his neighbour see him.

Harry, the neighbour, was not a man that liked to share his pleasures with anybody and was known to become quite cross if anybody vexed him.

Harry was a soldier and served his time on overseas postings, like anybody else in the defence forces.

That experience changed an already taciturn man into a gruff loner that withdrew so far into his own self that a barrow load of grenades would not bring him back.

He was long gone.

Which left his wife, Alice, in frustration, for she was a live woman with interests of her own that needed fulfilling. She mentioned this a few times to harry to no response.

Alice was not at all happy with Harry's assumed role of station manager and her eyes wandered to the twitching curtains of her neighbour's bedroom window. The signal was definitely red or green depending on how you look at these things.

Ned the neighbour was not a conventionally handsome man and he was not tall of stature; but like many small men before him he had an active libido that knew no conscience.

In fact his wife, who played no part in this story, had moved out some years past and taken their children with her. Ned was what you would call a married Irish bachelor.

He would claim single status in pursuit of romantic quarry; or marital status if the situation turned dangerous and the woman thought the affair should be placed on a more secure footing.

Ned's footwork in extracting himself from such situations was the stuff of legend.

The day he found himself locked in Harry's wardrobe while Harry prowled the bedroom was not such a situation.

Once inside the wardrobe Ned found it hard to get back out again in safety. His shaking body and chattering teeth did not help.

It began, as these things do, innocently enough.

Ned was aware that Alice was not a happy person and began to twitch his curtains whenever he knew Alice was wandering alone in the garden.

And that was as far as it went. That is, until Harry was sent to jail for a fracas that began over a game of dominos.

Harry was a top domino player. He had studied the theory of dominos and was an expert player of the game.

So, when a man from the next town accused him of cheating, in a pub tournament, Harry was annoyed.

And he said so, and demanded the other man apologise to him for the insult. The other man, who was known as an amadán of the highest order, refused all advice from others to apologise.

The issue was taken outside where a fight started between Harry and a pair of fighters from the same town as the amadán who was not so foolish as to get in the way of flying fists.

The amadán stood off to one side while the argument he had provoked progressed.

The gardaí arrived in force. But the pair managed to portray themselves as innocent bystanders attacked by a mad Harry.

Harry, in frustration when words of explanation failed him, swung at the sergeant in charge with his large fist. It was more to frighten him than anything else, he said later.

Harry connected with the man's jaw which gave way. Harry found himself in court the following morning with several more bruises than he had when he finished the first fight.

The judge sentenced him to jail for assaulting the garda and off he went, leaving his train set to fend for itself in the back garden.

Alice played the dutiful wife for a while and visited Harry in prison as often as was appropriate. But her heart wasn't in it. She'd been on her own with the kids often enough while Harry was overseas and she was not pleased to be on her own now that the kids were grown and gone and Harry was in jail over a silly game of dominos.

At his request she half-heartedly ran the train every so often to make sure it was not seizing up. Alice reported to Harry on the time it had taken to complete its scheduled run, not that it ever changed. She even took a shears and trimmed the grass around the level crossing, at Harry's suggestion, in case the points became covered.

All of which she related to a sympathetic Ned who leaned ever further over the party wall to hear what she had to say.

After a while, Ned found himself on Alice's side of the wall, the better to study the train layout and to assist her in its upkeep.

A while after that, and he constructed what he described as a tunnel of love in his garden that ended against the wall of Harry and Alice's garden. It was made of bamboo cane bent over to meet the canes from the other side to form an O through which people could walk without being seen.

With climbing plants festooned around it --- there came a time, especially in the month of May --- when few could see inside the tunnel.

Ned took to sitting inside the tunnel and whistling at Alice every time she donned her station master's hat to make Harry's train depart.

One whistle borrowed another and soon Ned was hopping over the wall and into Alice's kitchen.

Soon after that and he was whistling up the stairs and for a while after that he had little breath left to whistle with, at all.

One fine afternoon when early summer heat was high and Ned was teaching Alice some new cross-overs, the old soldier returned from prison.

He wasn't due home for another week Alice whispered. Ned wondered if he could get out the window without being seen.

As it happened, he could not; for the old windows had been replaced by nice draught-proof affairs that allowed neither access nor egress to human beings.

Into the wardrobe he went for there was nowhere else to go.

Harry arrived in the bedroom an saw a nicely-flushed Alice. Hequite naturally assumed that the breathless woman on the bed was as glad to see him as he was her. Harry lingered awhile in their room with Alice and neither of them mentioned train sets.

Time passed in this fashion, as it does.

Ned was sweating away on his own inside the wardrobe which he knew would turn into a coffin if Harry wanted a change of clothes and opened the door.

Ned doubted that Harry would listen to any explanation as to why there was a man in his wardrobe while he was supposed to be still in jail.

Ned believed ever afterwards that he lost so much weight through sweat and fear in that wardrobe that he began to lose height from his brief stature as well from that moment on.

In the room Harry reached the end of the line. Tired of the excitement and he wandered down the stairs and out to his outdoor train set.

Alice let Ned out of his temporary prison and out of the house, unnoticed by Harry. Ned hopped off home.

Romance can turn on the spin of a coin, on a breath wrongly taken, a word misspoken.

Alice seemed disappointed in neighbour Ned now that Harry the warrior was back and the train was running on time once more.

Harry gave up dominos and bought an extra engine for Alice to run and they began to speak about flyovers, tunnels, sidings and the like.

Some time later, the tunnel of love burned down; but nobody was able to say for sure who owned the petrol can that was found at the scene.

By then Ned had taken up indoor bowling and was rolling after a woman called Áine whose wrist action he greatly admired.

And Alice was corresponding by email with a submariner she met on Facebook called Fritz.

Harry for his part sat in his garden and smiled a lot and ran his train on time.

There are some things that even grown-up boys enjoy more than others.

Miracle on the Road to Dodsboro

In these days of global warming, when we seem to have no recognisable seasons at all, it's as well to remember when a winter was a winter and there was a time at the end of winter and the beginning of spring when east winds blowing from the steppes of Russia could be expected to chase you home to the warm fireside.

Depending on the number of people in your family and the amount of seats available you might get near the fire to be warmed up. But you might not; and civil war could ensue, with repercussions for generations yet to come.

In those days, everybody sat in front of the fire slowly going red from the heat coming from the flickering flames while their backs froze as a consequence of the cold draught coming in around badly fitting windows and doors behind them.

In a crude form of air-conditioning, some people, when they were finished with the evening newspaper, flattened it out into strips and dropped the strips into the gap between the wall and the window frame where, in the summer, cooling breezes blew in around the house from the warm street outside.

Sometimes, the cold in the winter could be so bad that people went to bed to stay warm in the depths of the coldness. They snuggled deep underneath a pile of overcoats for heat in much the same way as a small animal hibernates deep in a burrow.

Hibernation rarely lasts however; for a touch of icy breath in the morning made lying on in bed a non-starter when it was warmer to get up and get out of the house and off to work where exercise warmed the blood a little.

As often as not, at a time when Ireland had four recognisable seasons to pass through in a twelve-month, roads at this time of the year could be icy and slippery.

Many a person going to work on a bicycle found themselves sitting on the ground with the bike on top of them, instead of the other way round.

If you were lucky enough to own a second-hand car then the slippery side roads had to be traversed --- always allowing that if your car didn't start; there would be no traction on the ice to drop the car into gear and start it up, as you flew down the hill.

There was no use in asking neighbours to get behind you --- for you could be pushed all the way to work with the car never starting at all, under hazardous conditions.

And you didn't want to take responsibility for old Tom's replacement hip breaking once more, if he fell at the back of the car on the ice.

When the more prudent drivers knew a cold snap was on the way they prepared well. No old coats were ever thrown out in those times. They were passed through the ranks of a family as somebody grew out of them and when there was no further use for them and if they were still sound they were passed to some other family to begin a new journey.

When they could no longer be worn out of doors they were used as bed covers and as door stoppers of winter draughts and finally the well-worn overcoat found its way into the motoring division of the family.

To counteract freezing conditions old overcoats used to be placed over the car's engine at night to keep the frost from attacking the water within. It was a common practice.

Sheets of cardboard were slipped underneath the engine to keep the rising frost in the morning from attacking the water in the engine block and cracking the self same block with icy certainty.

Methodical drivers drained the engines at night of all water and then filled them back up again, in the morning, as if they were horses being fuelled for the day.

When anti-freeze came along, and it was no longer necessary to drain water from a car at night, it was akin to colour television arriving in the first house in the town. People knew it worked but not quite how.

A radiator that was holed by a spiteful frost was a problem. Water ran out of the radiator as soon as it was poured in the top. Shoes could suddenly become very wet indeed.

A leaking car or lorry or van had to keep stopping at the public water pumps along the road in to the city to top up for fear of seizing up, from the heat of it all.

The only example of such public assistance to motorists still standing is the public water pump at the foot of Chapel Hill in Lucan where many a motorist filled a thirsty car on a summer's day.

Installed as a public water supply for local houses, the pumps doubled as watering points for thirsty traffic and passers-by.

Everybody knew that a radiator could be fixed by breaking a few eggs into the water. The resulting concoction formed a membrane over the point where water was escaping, and a temporary repair was effected.

It got you home in just the same way that a nylon stocking could be used as a surrogate fanbelt if the fan belt failed in the car and the whole enterprise started to heat up for lack of a cool breeze.

Bella, a woman driver, who was separated from her husband, in a time when this was an unusual circumstance, managed to achieve the same result by using her ex-husband's underpants as a fan belt, in an emergency.

He was a big man, her husband; but she never quite explained how his underpants came to be in the car; or even if they really belonging to her husband.

Or if that was the true cause of the estrangement.

Her estranged husband, Gerry, was amenable to earning a few extra pounds by delivering some coal with the local coalman.

He was only called on to render this service when pressure was on and coal deliveries needed to be done in something of a hurry because of a climate change as in it was going to lash snow and nobody would be able to move on the roads for a few days.

Gerry was an atheist by persuasion and could never see the point of organised religion at all. He had wanted to marry his ex-wife in a field by a lake when the sun was shining; but she had insisted on a church wedding and a bit of a do in a hotel afterwards.

Which might have been another reason for their parting of the ways.

Gerry's views on religion meant that the coalman kept Gerry away from any deliveries that included calling to a member of the clergy with home heating fuel.

For Gerry would ask of an icy January night of an unsuspecting clergyman how he could prove there was a God and if he could did God say it might snow before morning?

The coalman was friend to all and had no intention of allowing Gerry to antagonise members' of the clergy who were all good customers.

On one fine January night Gerry and the coalman were late finishing deliveries in Dodsboro and when they turned for home the roads were already covered by a sheen of ice with no sign of anybody arriving from the county council with shovels of sand to lessen the dangers.

Neither was there any sign of the Lucan by-pass being built at this time; so the road from Dodsboro ran in a straight line down the then intact Tandy's Lane.

On the left was a very high wall behind which a construction industry operation was based.

They started down the hill in high good humour with a now-empty lorry and tired limbs. About halfway down the hill the ice became so thick that the coalman and Gerry found themselves facing back up the hill in the cab of the lorry while the lorry flew backwards down the hill in an out-of- control skid.

A man walking up the hill observed this phenomenon with equal amounts of fear and wonder and considered if he could levitate up and over the wall to avoid certain death.

He could not.

Instead, he made the sign of the cross and started to make an act of perfect contrition at the end of his useful life.

A terrified Gerry observed this as the coalman managed to swing the lorry back onto its correct trajectory, which meant that the occupants were now facing forward once more; but still tore past the man, whose name was Luke, as he prayed away.

The coalman was otherwise an excellent driver and managed to bring the lorry to a halt before it careered through the walls of Lucan Demesne at the foot of the hill.

Gerry hopped out when the lorry stopped and said he'd walk from there.

It was only four miles home. He would get there in no time if he slid. The coalman drove off in the direction of his depot to park up for the night.

Life assumed its normal tenor and the coalman forgot about the skid as just another occurrence in the life of the town.

But, Gerry took to attending early mass every morning and even offered to take up the collection for a surprised parish priest, who still wondered how he could know if it was going to snow or not..

If Paul had a conversion on the road to Damascus, then Gerry discovered on Tandy's Lane that night that it's never too cold to say a prayer.

Elvis is on the Phone

Eddie knew he should've let the phone ring in his house without answering it.

Eddie thinks of himself as an entrepreneur; but he is really just a stage beyond being an odd job man who sells this and that on the side.

So, the phone rings at odd times in his home which doubles as the head office of his mind.

Eddie had been watching business channels on satellite television and was greatly taken by a man who came from Buffalo in New York State and claimed he had been broke, as Eddie was much of the time.

What the man from Buffalo also claimed was that he had invented a system of running a home-based business and had made millions in the process.

That was how he now lived in a penthouse overlooking a big park in New York city.

What he didn't say was that he had made the money by selling the secret to making millions to other people in the form of six overpriced CDs sold as a set with a loose-leaved folder to go with them.

The CDs consisted of him talking for hours on end on how easy it was to make money --- without quite specifying how he did it. Eddie bought the CDs and listened to them and then made up one of his own.

He placed an ad in the paper and sat back to wait for loads of people to give him so much money that he would soon be a wealthy man himself.

Except that the phone didn't ring that much.

A few people rang to ask how much the car was that he was selling and for a while he got cross with them until he found out that the car seller's number was identical to his, bar two numbers in the middle that were reversed.

So, he told them the car was sold, and he wasn't taking trade-ins.

But while he had them on the phone he had just a few CDs left to sell and did they want to know the secret to being rich?

Well, most people would like to know the secret to being rich. Of course they would.

But one of the callers pointed out to Eddie that a good way to be rich was not to spend any money at all and that was why she wasn't going to buy anything.

Eddie said she had rung up about buying a motor car and that was thousands, whereas his CD was priced in the tens.

She told him she was only asking about the car for her son who was in England and thinking of returning home soon. Would Eddie buy the car back if the son changed his mind about the colour?

That time, Eddie hung up the phone himself.

And thereafter he let it ring unanswered: so the phone went to voicemail. Except once.

Afterwards, Eddie believed that he knew before he picked up the phone that the caller was trouble. He should have let it go to voicemail.

"This is Elvis," she said when Eddie answered the phone, a little before midnight on Thursday night.

A woman calling herself Elvis could not possibly be the full shilling, no matter how plausible her explanation for anything might be.

He was already putting the phone down when he heard her ask how much he was asking for the CD?

"What?" Eddie asked, in spite of himself, though he knew it was daft.

"How much is the CD that you advertised," she said again in such a soft voice that Eddie wondered if he was speaking to a young man rather than a female.

He said the price and gave her a few sentences of sales introduction, despite his doubts.

Elvis asked more questions and Eddie by now reckoned he had a sale. And money from Elvis was just as good as money from anybody else.

But after a while, Elvis seemed to stop listening to Eddie.

He would have stopped the sales pitch except he knew Elvis was alive on the other end of the line. He could hear him breathing.

"Where will I send the CD?" Eddie asked in an attempt to get the person to close the sale and make an order.

"To be honest," said Elvis, without a trace of an American accent, "I don't really want to buy the CD."

Eddie tried a few more ploys to get Elvis to show a little more sustained enthusiasm. But it was like playing a guitar with no strings. All action and no sound, never mind a missing echo.

Then, Elvis said: "Would you like to talk to me?"

It was almost midnight and Eddie needed sleep but there was a chance of a sale. After all, Elvis had rung him. And asked about the CD.

If he could make the sale and offer a little discount to Elvis to allow the name be used in merchandising and endorsement he could make millions by next week, never mind by the end of the year.

The conversation wore on through what was Eddie's favourite film of all time?

"Casablanca."

His favourite book?

Eddie spied his wife's latest reading material on a table and said "Cecelia Ahern's ... *P.S. I Love You*."

There was a pause during which Eddie wondered if his wife was in bed yet or had she just heard him say: "I love you," to somebody on the phone?

"Do you, Eddie? Do you love me true?" asked Elvis.

Apart from the fact that she had just called him Eddie when he had not told her his name; Eddie was now very cross.

He was sure it was some pal's wife, or girlfriend, setting him up.

So, he hung up the phone and went to the bedroom to find that his wife was fast asleep, as far as he could see.

But, she was awake, and ready for fight, a few hours later when Elvis rang back.

The phone was on that side of the bed and she reached it before Eddie could get there.

A sleepy hello was quickly followed by a sharp "Who are you?"

Eddie pieced the conversation together later from the safety of the spare bedroom to which he repaired after Elvis rang back several times demanding to know why Eddie's wife was sleeping in Eddie's bed.

The phone was disconnected by then, which only caused the voicemail to switch into answering mode and Elvis was recorded telling Eddie that they were destined for one another.

And when she told Eddie she would swing by the next time her tour brought her close to him; he wondered where he might purchase a gun for protection.

It wasn't the sort of thing you found in the classifieds section of the paper.

On the other hand, he might not need a gun if he could persuade his wife to meet Elvis instead, face to face. He knew Elvis would not be the last woman standing.

But, asking his wife if she would like to meet Elvis didn't seem such a bright idea.

She was convinced that Eddie was playing away from home and that only she had answered the phone to his lover she would never have known the truth.

That the other woman had said she was Elvis only added fuel to the fire. She was a mocker.

Elvis didn't ring for a while after that first night and Eddie gave up selling the CDs in favour of a carpet cleaning franchise he thought he had invented after watching a demonstration on a shopping channel, one wet Monday morning.

Then ages afterwards the postman arrived with a large card for Eddie.

It was from Elvis.

His wife was out shopping, so Eddie ripped open the large card to find a love letter to him enclosed.

Elvis said she had been away for a while and apologised for not completing the purchase of the CD. She was on her way back to him and was really looking forward to meeting up with Eddie, once more.

Eddie who like a lot of people if they were being honest had never met Elvis in the flesh wondered what she looked like, and if she dressed the part and if she would consent to having her picture taken for a new CD brochure.

But, to be on the safe side he burned the card in the fireplace before his wife came home.

After all it would be a bit awkward to say: "Elvis wrote to me."

He had only recently made it back to the marital bed; but a cuddle remained out of the question.

Meanwhile, he checked the phone to see that it was re-connected.

He wanted to be the first to pick it up the next time Elvis rang.

Eddie had an idea for a golfing DVD he was going to market and he thought he might call it The Strokes of Elvis.

All he needed Elvis to say would be "Ahuh" on the promo and he would sell millions.

No doubt about it.

Kidnapped Streaker

A man can be naked without being a streaker. He can run along a street without any clothes and not be a cause of public offence.

At least, that's what Niall told the judge and his smiling court. Niall was pleading not guilty to public indecency, at the time.

Niall's appearance in court began with small steps. Each small step led on to the next small step and before any of the six other people at the stag party was aware, it had all become a large step to their appearance together in court.

Niall was first cousin to Sammy who was getting married. To save money Sammy had his stag party in his own house. Samantha, his wife-to-be had allowed herself to be persuaded to go to Paris with her pals for a hen-night on the same weekend as the stag, so as to clear the space for the boys night in.

Which was why Sammy loved Samantha: she was so understanding, and accommodating.

But, given that nobody is a saint and nobody is perfect; she was also a bloodhound who noticed anything amiss, so a stripogram was out of the question.

That suited Sammy down to the ground, for he had developed a paunch and he had no wish to show his naked belly to his pals while a fat woman, who mostly didn't know which address she was at, struggled out of her clothes, for payment, while the others cheered or clapped.

Instead, they ordered in loads of drink and Skinner brought along a few DVDs that were for their eyes only. They all cheered again and whooped as the credits rolled; but after a while they grew jaded with the same old thing going on forever. The subject is not a spectator sport and palls soon enough if there is no personal participation.

It was Skinner's idea in the first place to go out for chips, which more or less led directly to the day in court.

Niall said there was plenty of food in the house and what was the point in going out?

Skinner said this was different: they would all go together to get their own food.

Six of the magnificent seven decided they would each go to the take-away and order chips and a burger and return to the party in the house.

Sammy said if he was going, he would carry his own food home. After all, it was his party; though Niall was at pains to point out to the court that Sammy had not suggested the nude shopping trip in the first place.

Earlier, they settled down to watch the Jack Charlton years DVD on the plasma screen in the master bedroom.

Sammy warned them to take their shoes off when they sat on Samantha's bed and not to spill any drink on the bed.

They all took their shoes off; but Skinner was the first to go naked with his feet. He said he thought the fibres from his socks might tickle Samantha when she returned from her lost weekend in Paris.

Sammy asked what *lost* weekend? but he was shushed by the others while they watched *that* penalty over and over as if it could be different the next time they saw it.

Niall was sleeping when he heard a shouting match going on in the kitchen between Skinner and two others. All three were well on at this stage and not making a lot of sense. But that didn't stop them arguing nonsense as if they were three wise men engaged in debate of importance.

The DVD was by now switched off in the bedroom and Niall was lying on the return of the stairs without shoe nor sock on either foot, he discovered to his surprise.

Somewhere along the line, it seemed, everybody had discarded their socks as well as their shoes; so 14 bare feet padded about the house.

Niall heard the words *hunter, gather, real men, dare,* and *chips* being tossed about as the argument grew stronger. It was all daft and did not relate to a football match as far as he could work out. it was all noise.

Eventually there was a shout of ..."Right," from what could only be Skinner's voice and a chorus of "right" from other voices with a submerged "no, are yiz crazy?" coming from what sounded to Niall like Sammy's slurred voice.

Whatever it was, Niall was on the no side in this referendum. Skinner was mad. So it was no surprise to Niall that when he arrived in the kitchen Skinner was naked.

Totally. So were four others without clothes and Sammy was down to a pair of boxers that said "Darling" across the front.

Niall had a vague idea that the word had been hand-stitched onto the boxers; but he was too woozy headed to be certain.

And he certainly was not going to look any closer to find out.

He was asked what he thought and six pairs of eyes turned towards him for an answer.

"Think about what?" He asked.

"We're going to the chipper for food; are you in like a man, or are you out like a girl?" Skinner asked in the manner of one that expected a shouted answer in the affirmative.

Niall looked at Sammy who believed this was his stag party and he should be in charge; but didn't quite know how to do that.

He asked why they were going out for food when the kitchen was full of the stuff ?

A few more drinks might make sense; for the well could run dry when there were no watering holes left open; but more food left him cold.

Skinner said it was a question of living off the land. Niall asked them all where their clothes were gone while he had been asleep. They were watching a match as far as he knew, then they were standing in the kitchen with no clothes on, talking about hunting for food in the take-away.

"No!"

It dawned on him at about the same time that Skinner nodded and said to the others:

"Take him, men."

They came at him in a confused blob

Niall tried to get away but they were too quick for him and before long he had joined them in their birthday suits. Even Sammy's Darling was now gone. Sammy was red as a beetroot; but it didn't seem to make much difference to anything that was happening.

There was a chance that he was blubbering as well, or he might have been singing a football song from Jack's glory days.

It was hard to tell with Sammy.

Niall shouted that they might take his clothes but they would never take his liberty.

"What liberty?" Skinner enquired.

"The liberty to say no," Niall shouted as the front door opened onto the street and the naked men jogged out of the building in single file.

He watched in horror as Skinner placed Niall's clothes firmly in a back pack and slung it over his shoulder so that Niall could not retrieve it without a naked scramble for the prize.

While he hesitated he was pushed out by somebody and he heard the door slam shut.

He thought about hiding; but then reasoned, as only a man in great confusion can reason, that he would be better to hide in plain sight among the six running bodies.

Niall took off after them down the town to the take-away. He had a late start and by the time he caught up they were all queuing at the high counter where the serving staff could only see the tops of their heads.

One by one they were served until Sammy walked out with his purchases, after leaving a fistful of crumpled notes on the counter as payment for all the others.

The street doors were automatics and when Sammy misjudged his timing on the way out they began to close before he was fully out. He yelped a little as cold glass on the street side connected with his backside.

A member of staff noted his boxer-less bottom and shouted at him.

Sammy ran away and before long the others were exposed as being fellow emperors without clothes and the gardaí were called.

They fled before dangers as hunter gatherers must do according to Skinner who said it was the only course open to them.

But Niall was still trying to catch his breath from the run down and did not make it outside before the owner locked the door with him inside the shop.

The others were followed by speeding gardaí to Sammy's house and arrested before they could get their clothes back on; for none of them knew who owned what.

They appeared in court the next day in forensic overalls supplied in the interest of fair play by the gardaí.

All pleaded guilty and were fined nominal sums with a dire warning that two o'clock in the morning was no time to be looking for chips on a naked stomach.

However, Niall pleaded coercion and was therefore not guilty, he insisted to the judge.

After a while of staring at Niall and the others the judge agreed with him and asked if he wanted to prefer charges of naked kidnapping against the others?

But since Niall could not say who had grabbed him or what had happened with any certainty he said he could not be a witness to his own kidnapping.

The judge found him not guilty and dismissed the case against Niall.

He avoided the eyes of the other formerly-naked men. But Niall did not go to the wedding.

He couldn't face Sammy in his formal wedding gear. The memory of the darling boxers was too much for him.

Skinner gave an after dinner speech that was wildly clapped by all the men at the wedding; but which made no sense to anybody else who sat on their hands, having read the report of the case in the local *Clarion*.

Samantha just smiled, there were no local reporters in Paris. After all, what happens in Paris stays in Paris.

Of course, the naked chipper is different.

Bag of Cats

What happens in the dead of night is for cats to know and humans to wonder at.

A cat's howling can be intense when feline romance prowls the back gardens. Humans not having cat's eyes to see in the dark are at a loss as to what is going on. Mostly, the cats come home the following morning in some shape or other, and refuse to speak about the night before. But when a family pet goes feral life changes for all concerned.

The newly liberated cat is not circumscribed by human mores and may converse with as many tomcats as she can find --- with the inevitable bags of wild kittens, raring to go in due course.

The nights are long, the companions many and offspring will be born to a wild way of life few domestic cats experience.

They are born free.

Sadly for them the territory they inhabit has been colonised by a stronger animal: the human being who will not tolerate long nights of screaming cats and long days of hissing felines when anybody approaches their patch.

It happened that a while ago, in the town, an eccentric lady who lived with neither chick nor child passed away in her sleep. Her collection of miscellaneous cats escaped from the confines of her home and quickly became intoxicated with the heady scent of freedom.

Nobody minded much for it took away responsibility of caring for the cats, or disposing of them.

All went well until they grew to be too many and turf wars began between the various cousins.

Two gentleman of the town, Hughie and Bobby, were engaged by local householders to rid the area of the plague of cats which threatened public order and a night's sleep for all.

Neither Hughie nor Bobby had what you might call a permanent job. They described themselves as contractors; though what sort of contractors they were was anybody's guess.

No contracts were ever signed nor witnessed and all payments were in cash.

They were asked to quote for the removal of the cats and they did so carefully and fairly and added a little bit extra for luck. They were duly hired to rid the area of all wild cats.

On the day, Hughie warned all cat owners to keep their loved ones indoors, otherwise who knew what unfortunate cat would be collected in the round-up. And neither Hughie nor Bobby would undertake to retrieve a moggy taken away by mistake.

"One in, all in," said Bobby who was a man of few words and whose hands and fists were very large for his body size. As a consequence, few argued with him.

Bobby owned the car and while Hughie liked to refer to it as *the* car, Bobby was always very careful to call it *my* car.

Hughie had acquired a number of large bags of the type used to carry coal around in. He also possessed industrial strength handling gloves, as part of his basic equipment for all jobs.

He held a bag open while Bobby grabbed a hissing cat and threw it at Hughie who expertly lifted the bag to catch the flying cat.

Each cat went tumbling head downwards into the maw of the bag.

Before they had time to turn around and race back out again the opening was closed on them by Hughie.

It was no use a wily cat waiting for the next body to come hurtling in and escaping that way for the next cat was just as cross as the first one. There were four legs, a tail, a body and a hissing head to contend with each time.

Bobby also used industrial gloves to catch the surprised cats and when they sunk their sharp teeth into his hand they met the tough resistance of the gloves; an occurrence that surprised them no end.

The bag began to grow heavy and Hughie said they had enough. But Bobby was a conscientious contractor to the last. If he took on a job he stuck with it.

When he was finished there would be no wild cat left uncaptured.

Hughie said again that the bag was getting very heavy.

Bobby ignored him. But he had to admit defeat when a marmalade cat and its deep-black cousin both escaped and headed for the next parish until peace was restored.

Bobby took the bag of captured cats from Hughie and marched with it hanging from one hand to his car.

He opened the back door of the four-door and pitched the squealing cats in headfirst by emptying the bag before slamming the door once more.

Bobby handed the now-empty bag to Hughie and told him to stop messing about.

Hughie said: "There's loads of bags and what you should have done was tied the bag of cats closed and used a fresh one for the next lot."

Bobby was now gotten into the swing of it and headed off with more bags to collect more cats.

Kids from everywhere turned up to observe the spectacle of the released cats bouncing from one window to the next inside the car in a vain attempt to escape.

The cats were like goldfish out of water and hurtling around in the same demonic manner as a fish fighting for life.

Little did they know that Hughie and Bobby meant to ensure the cats slept that night with the fishes in the nearby canal.

The partners filled another pair of bags and Bobby emptied them into the car to the wonderment of an incredulous Hughie who eventually asked, just what was to happen next?

"We'll drive them as they are," said Bobby.

"Drive them where?" asked Hughie who was now as alarmed as he had ever been at Bobby's grasp on sanity.

"Away," said Bobby quietly in case he frightened the children who were now openly speculating on the life expectancy of the cats in the car.

Hughie said he was not getting in the car and Bobby said: "Alright but you won't get any share of the money, in that case."

Hughie would have argued the point; but Bobby hopped into the driver's seat and slammed the door shut.

He started up the engine and the mad cats --- momentarily stilled by the presence of a human in the car --- began bouncing about once more, once the engine settled down and the broken exhaust subsided to a dull roar beneath them.

Bobby revved the car impatiently. To the gathered crowd, it sounded like the warm up grid for a Formula-I race. Hughie, seeing his share of the cash driving away, took a breath, crossed himself and jumped in. He slammed his door three times to make sure it was shut, tight.

He pulled his jacket over his head so that he looked like a poor imitation of the hunchback of Notre Dame in a school play.

The cat contractors drove off in the car with the cats still leaping from one window to another.

Hughie stayed quiet on the off chance that they would not see him and attack him, instead of the seat's upholstery.

It was a fine plan.

Take the cats from one area to another and drown them as expeditiously as possible.

Job done.

Mission accomplished.

However.

And it was Hughie that pointed out the however. All of the cats escaped once more from the car on the bank of the canal, they having arrived there, and opened the door to get out with only a few deep scar scratches to their skulls..

The men stood watching the cats disappear frantically to anywhere but into the black water alongside.

They should have kept the cats in the bag when they caught them said Hughie said in his best non-aggressive voice. It was more of a sorrowful tone, if anybody had been listening.

Otherwise, he said warming to the subject in the face of a silent Bobby; how were they going to get them out of the car and into the canal?

Bobby said nothing but Hughie knew that he was as cross as a bag of cats at seeing the whole lot escaping along the canal.

That is, until Hughie remembered a man with a factory that had a lot of trouble with rats in the area and was looking for a quote on getting rid of them from Hughie and Bobby contractors and pest exterminators.

If they moved quickly enough and nobody noticed the plague of wild cats newly arrived they could replace one plague with another, and be paid twice.

They could claim to have rid the area of the rats. In time, they might return to move the cats, once more.

Bobby took out his mobile phone and began dialling.

Bobby was good at crisis management.

Hughie knew that. It was why they were partners.

Mothers can be liars too

Irish mothers tell a lot of lies in their time not least to their offspring. Quite why they have a special day set aside for them, every year, without exception, is a mystery to the many men who are not mothers.

For the truth of it is that without a willing man there would be no mothers, a fact often lost sight of in the hullabaloo about getting the mother figure into a restaurant for lunch and out again once a year without unduly raising tempers and blood pressure and causing a rift in the family that could last for a thousand years.

The Hallmark image of mothers as benign creatures surrounded by their chirping chicks as they saunter forth on a sunny Sunday in March to claim the high ground can be puzzling for those who take a middling and fair view of the whole affair.

Restaurants are booked ages in advance and calendars and diaries checked so that orbiting offspring can be brought together to wish the mother figure a happy Mother's Day along with all the other mothers who subscribe to the notion of a special day for one member of the family.

Fathers get a day too, true enough, to balance matters out and in recognition of their role in the preservation of the species. But not so you'd notice really.

For men are today what small children were once upon a time: there to be seen but not heard. Their role --- while not a passive one --- is supposed to be silent; beyond a polite "thank you", every now and then.

That aside, it has been a source of wonder for many why there is not a granny's day or a grandad's day since they are the mammy's mammy and daddy respectively. Some say there is a grandparents' day but if there is, it's kept quiet.

There is no sister's day either or a brother's day or an uncle's day or a day for good old Auntie Vera, for that matter.

So, Mother's Day it is, for few mammy's wave their hand to say: "Count me *out*."

Mothering Sunday is celebrated in Britain as the mid-point of Lent and by the greeting card industry everywhere as a spring fillip for sales.

In Ireland, we celebrate the middle of Lent with St Patrick's Day which now runs for a week or so, depending on how lucky you get on the big day.

But we also celebrate Mother's Day as well, so as not to miss out on a day for feasting and rí-rá and telling lies about our mothers.

On that day, everybody's mother is a pure saint. She is the fount of wisdom and knowledge, a benign homely person, always there no matter what happens and no matter what the catastrophe may be that befalls one of her care.

That she was also somebody who made it all up is often overlooked. For some are better at mothering than others.

Bobby the shoemaker is a case in point.

Over the years Bobby was in more than one argument on the effect of sun showers with those who hung around his shoemaker's shop for gossip heat and some comfort on a winter's day.

For Bobby's mother told him one summer time it is not possible to get wet in a sun shower.

She went further and told him that it was a scientific impossibility to get soaked to the skin while the sun was shining down on you.

This she told him on a particularly hot summer's day when her husband and Bobby's daddy who were the same man arrived home early from work. He said he was very warm and that Bobby's Mammy looked very hot herself, in her light summer attire, and sandals with the peep-through toes.

Bobby was sent to the shops to buy a lucky bag and told to play in the puddles on his way back, for it would do his feet good, according to his father, who was also something of an expert in his own right.

Bobby checked with his mother to see if this was correct for his father was known to tell an odd fib, just for fun.

The mammy, however, had gone somewhere to comb her hair, in the middle of the day.

When Bobby said it was pouring rain and in normal circumstances he was under strict orders not to get wet, in case his hair turned rusty and he became a redhead with a short temper, he was told by both parents that it all depended when the rain fell, in what circumstances and at what temperature. And today the temperature was very high.

It followed that sun-warmed rain was therefore harmless to small boys.

Bobby went and got wet and caught a cold and spent several very warm summer days in the bed with a high temperature. His father said it was most likely there had been something in the lucky bag that didn't agree with him.

When Bobby grew older and borrowed a book from the library and discovered that boys of his age in books were receiving pocket money he thought this a great idea and mentioned it to his mammy.

The mammy soon found out which book it was in who wrote it where he got it and which librarian was on duty when he got his hands on it and when it was due back.

This she did so she could save Bobby the bother of bringing the book back to the library himself and being offered something similar in the library.

Quietly she told him the sad tale of a local teenager now left the town who had read that book and had put it to his parents that he should have something similar in the form of disposable income.

His mother agreed and gave a few coins to the happy chap.

Imagine said Bobby's mammy in a tone of shocked outrage how terrible a thing it was that happened afterwards.

"What?" asked an almost speechless Bobby, a little excited and frightened as this revelation of a whole new aspect to life beyond lucky bags and watery puddles unfurled from the woman he trusted more than anything in this world.

She named two teenagers who were now young men with jobs of their own; but who nearly went to prison for life for the offence except for the intervention of Mr Adams from the other end of town.

According to Bobby's mother they each took an ankle of the small boy and hoisted him up to shoulder height to shake him silly until the coins in his pocket rolled free. Whereupon they dropped him on the ground and made off with his money.

The mammy fell silent at that point while she and Bobby pictured the scene.

That it should come to this.

Bobby was very grateful when his mother told him she would not put him through that ordeal by giving him pocket money that could be stolen from him.

And so it went on and when Bobby got a little older and realised that Mr Adams used to be a Catholic and was attending Protestant services on a Sunday with his Protestant wife, he asked his mother another question.

If somebody is a Protestant and becomes a Catholic what would you call them? "A convert," his mother replied without a blink.

"And what then if he was a Catholic in the first place who decided he would become a Protestant?"

"He would be a pervert," said his mother with all the conviction of somebody who knows nothing about anything.

Bobby thought to be a Protestant was a much more interesting way of life than being a Catholic, for he never doubted his mother's wisdom or knowledge.

For perverts in those more innocent days were understood to be men who wandered outside the confines of their martial setting to indulge in a little fishing now and again in a different stream. That and many more such strange goings-on Bobby understood to be the preserve of people his mother warned him to stay away from, lest he die roaring.

Then, a famous English actor died and in a retrospective montage of clips of his films on television Bobby saw the said actor as a young Oliver Twist being hoisted up by two teenagers until coins ran from his pockets and they made off with his money

Bobby was aghast.

For he knew if he told his mother that a famous director had stolen her true story she would never forgive the director.

That the director had originated the story; and not that his mother had seen the picture in the local picture house and adapted it to circumstance, never occurred to Bobby.

Such is the stuff mothers are made of. For somebody else's lies are a mother's well-meaning intervention in the life of her children, designed not to deceive; but to protect.

Still.

When the sun is shining and the rain is falling, Bobby now carries a spare cap in his pocket, just in case he meets a different mother with a different story to tell.

And he has turned off the television for there is no truth to be found there, as his mammy used to tell him whenever a person inside the set said something that disagreed with her view of the world.

Television comes and goes but mothers go on forever.

Summer time and the living is easy

Spring is a time for new beginnings when a town and its people shake off the slumber of winter and face the new seasons with anticipation. The clock changes to summer saving time. People are open to new ideas and new ventures. Days are longer, if nothing else.

Which is why chancers and confidence men use people's good feeling to persuade them it's a good idea to hand over cash for nothing. Just investing in the future brings hope of good times to come, for many; and who can blame them.

Some dishonest people don't ask for cash at all; they simply ask you to hand over your bank account details.

It's called phishing with a ph instead of an f.

Though loads of people say F after they have fallen for the dodge. Flip.

Phishing is an equal opportunities scam and anybody can be caught out with it.

Maria's ex-husband Bill was one of those who fell for the trick.

It came in the guise of a request to confirm details of Bill's entry in a directory that he had never heard of; but seemed like it could bring him loads of orders from people who wanted to avail of his in-store music business offering.

The catch was that he had to pay the sender loads of euros, this year, and for several to come as well, or be sued by the directory operators.

Bill did not realise this at first for he did not read the small print before signing and sending off the form.

The matter caused terminal friction between Bill and Maria. In fact, Bill moved out of the family home to live in the storeroom where he had a ganzyload of unsold CDs, just to get away from Maria's carping at his stupidity.

Bill sold CDs to store operators with pre-recorded music on them interspersed with Maria trilling about the wonderful bargains that were to be had in the shop this week.

The CDs were to be played to happy shoppers.

Sadly, few shopkeepers were thrilled with the idea. Sales of the CDs were lacklustre to nil.

Matters were not helped by Maria's distinctive voice being very recognisable. And shoppers, weary of the creeping vowels, went elsewhere when they heard her voice roiling down the aisles at them.

Maria of course did not agree that her voice was sending shoppers home without their groceries. Bill did not agree that his idea was daft in the first place; but both recognised that they were losing clients and nothing was coming in.

So, he went back to work selling lucky lines on charity cards around the country and pocketing the commission to be had.

If your number came up you won something more than you paid for the line. Elementary stuff.

He was away a good deal and even though they were estranged, Maria missed him.

The house was empty without him and if she was being very honest, it was too quiet without Bill's pottering about.

So, when Tony called to her house one early evening she was an opportunity waiting to be had.

Tony was a suave male of the most dangerous type. He looked like a man who needed taking care of; unlike other chancers who usually turned up neat and tidy and with a nice line of patter.

Tony looked like he would be better for a little direction in life. He was past the first flush of youth; but not yet arrived at the suburbs of middle age.

This air of need was his secret weapon; people were inclined to believe him when he spoke. And when he told of being an official collector for a good cause people took him at his word.

He looked like he was a good cause in himself, standing there, perfectly formed in a suit with a light jumper underneath it that looked like it needed replacing some time ago.

But Tony was thorough. He did not expect anybody to believe he was who he said he was. Not just on his word.

There were too many unsavoury characters around the place. These people existed to fleece unsuspecting parishioners who really should have known better. Nonetheless, they did not deserve to be robbed of their life earnings.

Maria nodded.

She now believed in divorce --- with a vengeance.

This man was perfect.

She insisted he come in and sit; while she made coffee for him.

Maria left him sitting in the over-furnished lounge while she tumbled upstairs to change her clothes, comb her hair and find some make-up that would intrigue her visitor.

Tony made a wonderful show of refusing hospitality when all he was really asking for was the lady's patronage.

Afterwards, Maria thought the word patronage had done it. Nobody had asked her to be a patron before. She thought it sounded quite nice, quite proper.

Tony explained that Maria simply had to sign up for a small monthly amount, no more than a few drinks a night, and the charity would benefit enormously. Children would smile and sing once more, water would flow, grass would grow, crops would sprout and the sun would shine, to the benefit of all.

Maria of course signed up and listened enthralled to Tony's tales of visiting the end user of all of this largesse and seeing the effect that even the smallest donation could make.

He only wished he could go there once more. But funds were low since he had taken on the responsibility of rearing his brother's two young daughters now that his brother had gone into rehab for his final chance at a life of his own.

Drink.

And when he said he would love to show Maria the project in person; Maria had a Bob Geldof moment.

She could see herself striding into the midst of adoring hopeless cases and telling them all was well; Maria was here.

But while she was mesmerised by the vista unfolding before her and wondering what to wear Tony stood up to leave.

He couldn't take up any more of her time; she had been generous in the extreme. He had to keep working; the good cause expected no less of him. His own income --- after tax ---depended on him attracting as much patronage as he could.

His emphasis on after-tax gave Maria a wonderful idea and she asked Tony to sit down and relax for a while.

Having made sure he was going nowhere; she went to the garage and opened Bill's underfloor safe. She extracted folding money and closed the safe once more.

When she turned to re-enter the house she found an embarrassed Tony behind her asking if he could use the bathroom.

She pointed him upstairs and told him to use the ensuite in her master bedroom " for handiness."

Tony vanished into the privacy of the house. When he returned Maria had made fresh coffee.

She absolutely insisted that Tony accept the cash. Most of it was Bill's anyway. It was a donation to his travelling expenses to the project.

Privately, Maria wondered what she would find when she googled the charity's location; it was important to be dressed appropriately. No use being a wealthy westerner in a poor area. It was bad manners.

Tony said he was lost for words and was even more pleased when she said she would make sure her friends all signed up to the charity's planned giving campaign.

Tony again said he was at a loss for words; but agreed to Maria's invitation to dinner. She explained that they could stay in and she would call the restaurant who would deliver whatever she ordered.

Later, he agreed to her invitation to stay the night when he explained that, as it was Saturday night, he had a night off from getting back to the two girls. They were on a sleepover.

Coffee gave way to wine. Tony stayed the night in the ensuite and Maria truly believed her ship had come in.

Tony was a man of charm and ability and said "Thank you," to Maria. Maria could have fainted with it the romance of it all.

She slept the sleep of the just and forgot all about changing her watch to summer saving time as all the television stations had warned her to do.

Newspapers had sternly warned of the dangers of sleeping late on account of the change in the clock.

You were supposed to arise an hour earlier in order to keep time with the newly-arrived summer.

Tony arose early and left while Maria slept in old time.

When Maria awoke, the bird had flown the coop, along with her jewellery, credit cards and the contents of the safe in the garage.

Tony the con was gone and with him Maria's hopes for the future.

And all she could think of was that she would not be buying a new outfit for her trip to the good cause.

That and how she was going to explain to Bill how a burglar had found his safe while she slept late into the long lonely days of summer.

Old Fools and Young Things

There is no fool like an old fool whether it's April Fool's day or any other day of the year.

But, some people whom you might take for a fool are not fools at all.

Andy, for instance, spent many years of his life in one mental institution or another on account of head injuries he sustained when he was assaulted by some people who disagreed with his strong political views. They believed that beating his head off the ground would prove they were right. They were wrong.

Molly his wife spent many hours visiting Andy in his various homes away from home as time passed.

She also took care of Andy's property inherited from his parents, who passed away while Andy was away.

Molly let them out to strangers. She kept the rents in cash, for she would not pay tax on what she considered to be her due. She told Andy she rented out the houses, and he was not to worry about the upkeep of their home while he was resting; all was looked after.

Andy eventually arrived home, many years later, in an old brown suit, a stubbled chin, shaved head and fixed stare. He said he was: "Very pleased to be home, thank you," to anyone that shook his hand in welcome.

So, Molly and Andy lived in peace and harmony in the time left to them. When Molly passed away, Andy suddenly found to his surprise that he was a very rich man, thanks to Molly's stewardship.

He found it hard to come to terms with new found wealth. He still rolled up newspapers to smoke them. He thought he could not afford tobacco, much less a full pack of cigarettes.

The taxman was unaware of the near-millionaire residing happily in the town. Andy continued to sign on each week for his state benefits. He was used to queuing.

Neither did most people realise he was rich, or they would have shook his hand more assiduously.

They thought he was a bit soft, actually.

Especially when he went to buy a set of wheels.

When he asked the salesman at the local car salesrooms if he could buy a motorbike off him the salesman laughed. With lots of winks to other salesmen he offered to show him a car instead.

But Andy wanted a motorbike. He had seen a man on a fine motorbike with black leathers when he was sent away for the first time. He remained impressed all through his years inside with the concept of a motorbike and a rider heading off down the empty road.

The salesman said he would rent him a car to see how he'd get on with it. But Andy said he would rather go somewhere else; where his cash would be appreciated.

To the salesman cash was a magic and a precious word. He said if Andy returned the following day, he would have some brochures for him and they could decide which model would suit Andy best.

By the following day the salesman had driven to a bike dealer and organised himself as a temporary commission agent for the dealership.

A week later Andy found himself leathered up with a helmet on his head and a motorbike between his legs.

The one thing missing was any experience of driving at all. This did not stop Andy putting the bike into gear and gunning the juice into it.

He took off, front wheel in the air, and was missing for two days during which he visited several cities in quick succession and slept in ditches beside the bike for company at night.

Andy was a happy man.

All went well for a while and he continued to dip into the biscuit tins of money that Molly had faithfully kept over the years.

After a particularly wet month of March, he'd had enough of the great outdoors and went back to the salesman to say he didn't want the bike anymore.

Andy said: "I want a car, a new one, but not a great big one, just something handy that I could learn to drive myself."

Now the salesman liked a commission as much as the next man but he also valued what he hoped would be a continuing relationship with Andy and handy cash.

He did not want to attend Andy's funeral any time soon. "I'll sell you a nice car on condition that you do one thing," he said.

"What?" asked a suspicious Andy.

"Take lessons in driving," said the salesman.

Which is where Eric came into the picture.

Eric did not like working in a structured way and often said --- to anybody that would listen to him --- that nobody should work more than three days in a week.

"Which three days of seven would be a matter of personal choice," he said.

Eric's one great talent was that he was a patient man and could teach anybody to drive anything. The deal he made with Andy was unique.

He would teach Andy to drive the new car; but since it was pointless for Andy to have a car that he could not drive then Eric would mind it for him when he wasn't teaching Andy to drive it.

Eric became the possessor of a car which he was free to drive wherever he wished and Andy became the owner of a car that he very rarely saw.

Eric advanced one excuse after another to an increasingly agitated Andy for his non-appearance at agreed times for driving lessons.

Andy dismissed him one Saturday afternoon when he heard that Eric went to the beach in the car instead of arriving for a lesson. Andy sold the car back to the garage for cash.

But, he fell out with the salesman who insisted that he take payment in a cheque.

"I don't trust cheques. I only want my cash back, or, as much of it as is fair," said a truculent Andy.

While he knew the salesman had overcharged him for the bike and the car, he put this down to stupidity on the part of the salesman who would never be more than a small time fiddler.

In the end, Andy told the astonished salesman to hold onto the re-payment as a credit against his next purchase.

He was now intent on buying a mobile home, for reasons of romance. Andy went to a different salesman and when he explained what had happened; the second man had the sense to see that he had a very good customer on his hands if he played his cards right.

So, Andy bought the mobile home through him after his new salesman had recovered Andy's money from the first salesman.

The second salesman even organised the hire of a crane to lift the mobile home into a field that Andy had purchased a little way outside town.

Andy had fallen in love and was quite excited.

The object of his affections was a young widow with two small children whose husband had been killed in an encounter with a train while he was walking along the train tracks one sunny day. The sun was in his eyes when he crossed the tracks. He stumbled and never arose again.

The woman lived in a mobile home on a narrow stretch of land beside the busy road. When Andy asked if there was room for another mobile beside hers she said that no land was available.

So he bought the five acre field behind the site and had his new mobile lifted by crane over his loved one's domicile and he made to move in.

However, since the gate to his new field was on a different road it meant that he would rarely see the woman he loved.

So he asked her if he could break down the fence and make a gateway to his home past her place. He got over-excited and suggested it would be their walk of love.

The woman felt a barring order would be best. The sergeant came to tell Andy that if he bothered her again he would be jailed immediately.

Andy was very upset at all of this. It seemed nobody was to be trusted.

At least inside the institutions he had dealt with people that were odd but who by and large were not dishonest.

The woman had been nice to him had smiled even asked him on one hot day if he would like a glass of water. He was sure he was in her affections. That's why he had bought a field, why he bought a mobile home ---- even though he had a fine house at home he could sleep in whenever he wanted.

Now, he was forbidden by law to approach her.

Andy decided to redress the balance.

On April Fool's day he rang the first car salesman's wife and told her the salesman was having an affair with the young widow, which he was not.

Observing the barring order he shouted across the road to the young widow that a madwoman had escaped from an asylum down the country, and was on the way up to see her.

She believed the widow was sleeping with the salesman who the mad woman thought was the madwoman's husband, he said helpfully.

And he told Eric that it had been confirmed that a man with AIDS had slept in the car.

He wasn't sure; but he thought the man died of AIDS since then and Eric should have a medical test and so should anybody else he had shaken hands with since Andy sold the car.

It was an April Fool's joke; but Andy was no fool.

He still had fourteen biscuit tins full of cash to spend and rents to collect every Saturday.

And there were plenty of other fish to fry as he always told Molly when she visited him.

The young widow barricaded the windows and doors of her mobile home against attacks by the salesman's deranged wife.

Andy rented out his five acres to a man who bred terriers. The all-night yelping kept everybody awake while he slept soundly in Molly's house and wondered what this Internet was all about that he kept hearing about.

Fishing, most likely, he thought as he went to sleep.

Love Letters in the Sand

Sometimes, we seek love in the wrong places.

We can be easily caught up in the swirl of springtime and young men's fancies turning to thoughts of love not to mention young women's fancies.

It's all got to do with the resurgence of spring and new growth and days growing longer and spring cleaning and turning over a new leaf.

Not to mention washing the windows or tidying up the DVDs in the sitting room.

For many people, the approach of St Valentine's Day is nothing more than trying to remember to buy a card and to post it before it's gone past its use-by date.

Nothing dates like an unsent Valentine's Day card.

For others, it's a reminder that a decision made in haste, long ago, is now here to repent at leisure.

For Alan Valentine's Day is a day for preparing for from a long way off.

Alan likes to mark the turning of another year with a reminder to himself that he is still available for love.

He is past the age where attractive women give him a second glance. That ritual where you see an attractive person and sneak a second look for pleasure and for wonder passed Alan by a few years ago. It happened around the time that his body began to thicken and his hair began to thin and he stopped wearing contacts in favour of a good pair of fashionable glasses.

It began to dawn on Alan, quite slowly, that younger women were more interested in men of their own age than in a man of some experience who had been around the block a few times.

This was brought home to him at a Hallowe'en disco when he worked his way through a roomful of women without persuading any of them to dance anywhere near him. None were in the first flush of girlhood. Some were in the throes of grannyhood. All said no.

He mentioned this to a few friends in work. Most agreed with him that the women did not know what they were missing. It was their loss, they agreed with Alan. But sure what can you do? You can't put an old head on young shoulders.

Alan was trying to keep a young head on his older shoulders; but the irony passed him by as his thoughts turned to the coming St Valentine's Day.

The company he worked for was a subsidiary of a large multi-national enterprise. It had open-plan layouts and games areas for staff to play in when taking a break. There was a strict ban on receiving personal post at work.

Alan had been hauled before his boss to explain why there was a substantial flow of mail arriving in the post room bearing his name. It was all marked private and confidential.

"It's anonymous, I don't know who is sending them to me" he told his boss.

But then a parcel addressed to him arrived with a ticking sound inside it shortly before the Christmas break. Security called in the army bomb squad to examine the package without contacting Alan in the first place. That was wrong he told them afterwards.

If they had done so, he could have told them it was a novelty clock somebody had posted to him in work, anonymously.

But a convoy of army vehicles had been and gone.

As had the television cameras wishing to know if the company was involved in any foreign lands the citizens of which might have travelled to here to make a loud point with a clock attached to something.

The simple reason for the ticking was that Alan was sick of getting rubbishy gifts from the pound shop as his present for Kris kindle.

He sent himself the clock which on the hour featured a Swiss farmer and a maid cavorting in a non-traditional Swiss clock manner.

It was to have been his way of showing he was still young and even if his body was aging his mind was forever young.

He would have the best of both worlds what with being risqué and innocent all in the one package. That is, if the fools hadn't evacuated the building and made the ground shake with a controlled explosion that tickled his feet.

Risqué and innocent was a package that Alan had been selling for years. He had run out of clients with the exception of a few half-daft work colleagues who never seemed to be able to get a lift home. They would ring his mobile to see where he was and could he do the honours, again.

Brenda from accounts was a particular problem.

That she was a single person and had never been on a date that anybody could remember was an additional problem. It was hard to get her out of his car at her house on those occasions when he left her home.

The clock was blown to smithereens and Alan was hauled before the boss of his boss to explain what was going on, and to say why his boss should not be fired along with Alan. Which seemed a bit harsh.

Once more, he claimed a lack of familiarity with the sender and privately thanked his lucky stars that he had posted it from a city-centre post office.

The matter was handed over to the Garda to investigate, by the company.

They had been involved anyway. It's not all that common to have an obscene Swiss alarm clock blown up at the front door with nobody claiming ownership of the thing.

The gardaí gave up after a while because the address label had been run off from a computer that could be found anywhere in the world.

They knew it was Alan who had sent it to himself. So too did his employers; but they needed proof if they were going to fire him without ending up with an unfair dismissals claim over sacking a man who was not only in love with himself, but was a waiting a response to his own letters.

Alan felt safe enough by February to buy the big red bear that played Love Letters in the Sand whenever you tilted it over.

There was new girl in the IT department whose name was Sharon, whom he quite fancied. The other day she had smiled at him and when he spoke to her she laughed and walked away. Alan knew he was in there. The Valentine's gift would be her's. He wished he could tell her now; but that would spoil the surprise.

He made sure there was enough time for the postal service to process it in time for the big St Valentine's Day that was approaching very quickly.

Alan wanted no pointless explosions, this time. He was in love.

Just in case, he made sure the address label was anonymous enough not to be traced back to him.

While he was standing in the post office queue with the wrapped teddy bear in his hand, who should he see smiling and waving at him only Brenda from accounts who was in town shopping.

She wanted to cadge a lift home. Whatever else happened when they got there would be in the lap of the Gods.

Worse, she pointed at the teddy in his hands as he tried to stand in front of the parcel to hide it.

Before he knew where he was, the loudspeaker had shouted "next" at him and rather than draw too much attention to his roaring red face he popped the teddy on the counter and asked the assistant if she could stick a larger sticker over the one addressed to himself and write in a new name.

He could not send the teddy to himself at work. Brenda would out him. Of that there was no doubt. She would now have to be the recipient of the stupid thing.

He just hoped that Sharon would understand and wait for him.

A mistake had been made he explained to the counter assistant. He had put his own name on the address label when he had meant to put a girl friend's name on it.

The assistant made the change and the valentine teddy began its journey to Brenda's heart.

Alan wondered as he walked away if she was any good at dancing at Hallowe'en?

Or, would she need private lessons?

Phantom coach

It becomes increasingly difficult in the weeks before Christmas to find a venue for a pre-wedding party.

Geraldine found herself in this situation when her chosen hotel closed down without notice. It left her with no reception venue and nowhere to have a hen party, just days before the stags and the hens were due to go on the tear.

Separately of course.

Geraldine and her fiancé thought it a good idea to book a three-in-one deal with the hotel for the reception and the two parties. It was a great idea; until the hotel closed.

The lads discovered a hotel in London. But since the hen and the stag party could not party together the hens remained in a quandary.

Eventually, one of Geraldine's pals found a hotel in Mullingar that had a cancelled stag party booking and was available.

How the party was going to get there was another matter. But, another pal knew a man who used to be a bank manager who now operated and drove a coach and was looking for work.

Rubin the bank manager had even acquired a minibus to ferry people to the main coach for big occasions.

Larry was his only staff member and he wasn't even staff. Larry preferred to be known as a specialist sub-contractor.

This meant he was a cash-only employee, that was his specialism. The sub-contracting meant he would drive for Rubin whenever the need arose.

Which meant that Larry was not always available to take the coach out when Rubin wished him to do so.

Knowing what Larry was doing at any time was like knowing which cloud in a storm would cover the moon's light. It was unpredictable.

Larry was a man who liked to swallow illegal substances. He was not foolish however and rarely smoked cannabis or dropped pills while driving the coach.

Except of course when he was on a long return journey and the party he was ferrying had sung itself to sleep.

He had the odd quiet smoke while the roads were clear and happy. If anybody noticed a smell, he said the tyres were rubbing together and the smell of burning rubber was a sweet one when experienced at a certain temperature.

On the night of Geraldine's hens' party Rubin was driving the smaller bus to collect the out-of-the-way guests. Larry was going through a bad patch at home and for once broke his cardinal rule on no drugs while he was driving people that were awake.

He abstained while he completed the school runs; but broke out a little when he did the active retirement association's bowling team's run out to Stillorgan.

They were lunatics to a man and woman who freed from the bounds of acceptable behaviour were up for the craic at any time. That their best male singer, Peter, had started on the long road to a new childhood and now thought he was a teenage crooner did not help.

Larry had to see that he did not sit in the back row of the coach where his wandering hands would creep around the back of the seat and grab the interesting bits of whatever woman sat before him.

That some of the mad biddies deliberately sat in front for to be grabbed did not make Larry's job any easier. Any time a female passenger screamed it was his duty to halt the coach, in the interests of health and safety, to ensure that all was well.

If he placed the culprit up front then Larry had to prevent him mooning at cars when they paused in traffic at traffic signals.

The effort would drive anybody to pot.

When Larry took the coach down to pick up Sandra his head was elsewhere. He knew they were going to Mullingar but forgot he was to collect more people and so he drove on with Sandra sitting in the back row, alone.

She was like a lost sheep with her tinkerbell headdress and her party horn bleating.

It happened that the coach in question had smoked windows.

The only place that had clear glass was the windscreen. Otherwise, it was very difficult to see in from the outside while those inside had a relaxed view of the passing world.

It was like having a first smoke. You weren't quite sure what was happening; you just knew it was nice and you would get sick any time soon.

Larry was a small man with a penchant for lolling in the seat even though he was driving. This also made him difficult to see.

An inebriated policeman standing on the corner would think the empty coach was travelling on its own.

It was only a short step from there to the firm conviction that it was a headless coach that had passed through the town.

Sandra could no longer see Larry in his driver's seat. This being the month of October and Hallowe'en being in the air Sandra was by now convinced that she was on a ghost bus. She reacted as any frightened person would react.

She called her very best friend and began to scream down the phone. Geraldine recognised at once that it was her very best friend Sandra. She thought Sandra was fooling around, so she disconnected.

Which made Sandra all the more frightened for a voice was now booming through the bus.

It was everywhere; it was coming out of the speakers and surrounding her.

It said: "Shut up, you're doing my head in."

Sandra screamed louder. But controlled it a little, for the voice had a local accent. She wasn't fully sure; but any ghost she had seen on DVD had an American accent.

The voice said: "If you keep screaming, I will stop the bus. I will pull your head off and throw it out the window."

Larry drove on, happy enough that the screaming had stopped. It was hard enough finding the road to Mullingar without a thousand voices shouting at him all the way.

Geraldine rang 999 to report that Sandra was missing; the coach was missing and she believed something had happened to her very best friend Sandra who never screamed on a phone in her life.

The duty garda, funnily enough, had just had a call from an ine-briated off-duty member to say the headless coach was in the town.

He asked for Sandra's mobile number which he rang straight away.

But Sandra fainted when Larry began to sing about going to San Francisco with flowers in his hair. She began to truly believe that she was on an unearthly journey in the solitary coach of death. Flowers were for the corpse she would shortly become.

Larry, growing weary of the incessant ringing, stopped the coach when nobody answered it. He picked up Sandra's phone and threw it out the door onto the middle of the road where it would be driven over.

He drove on and when he came to a village on the old road, for he was under Rubin's instructions to avoid the newer toll-road as not being cost-effective, he wheeled the coach into a large if dark car-park beside a pub that was closed down. It not only had no beer; it had no customers.

By now fed up with the journey, Larry left the coach and walked out onto the road to meet the local bus to Dublin. He boarded and soon fell asleep for the whole happy trip.

Sandra awoke on the headless coach to a great clattering of noise and a bright white light all about her.

Stepping from the bus she walked into the middle of the tarmac car-park to stand with arms aloft.

To the great white light, Sandra said: "Take me now. For I am ready."

A booming voice said: "Stay where you are. You are safe now. Is anybody else on the coach?"

"I came on my journey alone."

"Where is the driver?"

"There was none. It drove itself," said Sandra with all the con-viction of a deranged hen.

There were voices all around her now, in the shadows, telling her to remain calm, she was safe; but she knew that; for the white light had found her. She was saved.

Geraldine arrived in a car with lots of people in it. They told more people on mobiles where they were. Eventually everybody knew where they had found Sandra who had been lost.

Sandra was a bit disappointed to find she was still on the road to Mulllingar, when the situation was explained to her. But, there was always the rest of the weekend to look forward to and this had been a good start.

Larry was arrested at his home. He swore the bus was hijacked by a large rabbit and he came home to where he knew he would be safe.

Rubin dismissed him and swore he would only operate one coach in future.

The only problem was that word spread of the strange happening in the town. Rubin was inundated with bookings for the headless coach and he had nobody to drive it.

There's always a cloud in every silver lining.

Bertie's balls

Property going for sale should look its best in the auctioneer's window. Trimmed grass attracts sales. A garden that needs a haircut will lower the buying price; it doesn't make sense; but there it is.

Bertie explained this to Jack Ladd when he hired him to attack the briars in the garden of the house he had just inherited.

It had been a long time coming. Bertie was the only nephew of Aunt Ena a deceased maiden aunt whose house Bertie and Jack Ladd were now attempting to access through dangerous-looking greenery.

There were trees and bushes everywhere. Without exception they were out of control. Some looked like they had fallen from a horror film and taken root in Ena's garden.

There were so many because Aunt Ena was a shrub-cutting thief. She carried a pruning shears and a large tan-coloured shopping bag on her travels at all times.

Once she spotted a shrub or bush that she fancied she would stake out the house in a way that would make a burglar proud. When she was sure she would not be spotted she moved in. Snip, snip and that was it. The prize was hers.

She brought it home and planted it. Then she forgot about it in much the same way as an emperor conquered a new territory and when it was his and secured he forgot about the detail.

Nobody minded too much about Ena's secret life as a phantom snipper. They all knew and pretended not to see.

When she went into hospital, Bertie as the emperor-in-waiting solemnly promised he would make sure the gardens would retain their impeccable appearance once Ena it fell to his lot to cherish and develop the property.

It was a promise that almost made Ena change her will so as to leave the house and gardens to an animal charity, even though she hated all animals.

She knew her gardens resembled a madwoman's knitting. She liked it that way.

She knew her way through the maze and she could always see somebody was coming by the waving of the mad pampas grass above where the lawn might have been.

In a moment of increased madness Ena bought several full-size garden statues of Greek gods at a garden sale. They were unclothed, of course. But in keeping with the time they sported fig leafs on their private parts.

The statues were placed neatly on the manicured lawn before insanity overtook Ena and she let the garden return to nature.

Or, to the Garden of Eden, as she would have it.

The white statues silently stood to scarify anybody walking past. Few expected a silent white face to materialise from the bushes as they approached the hidden front door.

Bertie had a childhood memory of these statues. He had not seen them in years.

He emphasised to Jack that they were there and they were not to be damaged in the cutting back of the greenery surrounding the property.

"They are valuable for their intrinsic artistic merit, and could fetch a fine price if auctioned," he said.

"Fair enough," Jack said. "And what sort of budget do you have in mind for the Herculean task of finding them and preserving them?"

He asked this of Bertie with some firmness because it was a known fact in the town that Bertie did not have a bean. Being left a neglected house like this might also mean he had not received any cash with it, Jack guessed.

Though he might, and it was as well to ask.

To a man like Jack, accustomed to quoting prices directly to cash customers, the client's face was reference enough as to their credit worthiness.

Jack could read a face as well as any transient fortune teller could read a hand.

Things did not look well on the face of Bertie. Jack divined that he had no money. There was none on the way. Jack might get paid if the property ever sold.

"I'll need a deposit," he said firmly.

"For what?" asked Bertie. "You don't need to purchase materials, there's no cost to you to start."

"There's the cost of specialised equipment and the cost of having the overgrowth transported away from here in a skip, for environmental reasons," said Jack who was on home ground in this discussion.

"We don't need to transport it anywhere; once it's cut, it will shrivel and we can burn it then," said Bertie with the air of a man who saw no problems whatsoever with this arrangement.

"In the first place, burning it is illegal, under environmental regulations. There are spy satellites flying overhead just watching out for that sort of thing," said Jack. "And in the second, it takes ages for stuff to wither down far enough to be dry enough to burn and what about your statues' arses?"

"What about them. It's artistic, that, bare bodies 'n all."

"So it is; but if you set fire to the garden, you might burn down the house. The least that will happen is that the statues will be blackened from the fire and instead of having white statues; you'll have piebald statues, on one side; maybe the backside. I don't suppose many people would buy them then, other than people with an interest in punishment who might think the black streaks were lashes."

Bertie was no longer listening to Jack's wandering thoughts. Being a property owner was more complicated than he had thought.

"Give me a price then. No, give me two prices. One for clearing the garden and leaving the stuff around the back of the house; and the other for doing all that environmental nonsense."

Jack did so, off the top of his head, and knew problems would arrive, in time.

Bertie thought disposing of the cut vegetation was the same as sweeping dust under the carpet. Lift the corner and it would disappear. Put it around the back of the house and nobody would see it.

Jack held out for a cash deposit when Bertie said he would take the lowest quote and would pay in full when he returned from London where he had to go on business of his late aunt's.

They settled on terms and some money changed hands. Bertie went off about his business and Jack laid into the garden.

Using a borrowed chain saw he cleared the ground in a day and a half. A job he told Bertie would take weeks.

Jack knew Bertie was not coming near the place until the garden was cut and the debris was burned, environment or no environment.

For he knew who Bertie had paid to set fire to the mound of felled wood and shrub when it was all pulled around to the back garden.

Dan Mac was a simple soul who when brains were given out was at the cleaners and missed it all.

Jack made a point of finding out which night Dan was not available to help him with some odd jobs. That night, Jack made sure to make a show of himself in the local hotel when he insisted on attending a ladies weight watching session on the grounds that not allowing him to weigh himself amongst the women constituted sexual discrimination.

The gardaí were called and Jack made a show of bravado sufficient to have himself arrested and held in the garda station overnight.

So, everybody knew where he was when Bertie's house went up in flames along with the debris from the garden.

Investigating gardaí found a petrol can on the ground and when Danny Mac turned up the next day with singed eyebrows and a fresh haircut he was arrested.

He swore he had tried to put out the fire because he was a close personal friend of Aunt Ena. In time, no charges were presented against him.

The problem that Jack faced and he had guessed it from the start, was that Bertie would renege on his agreement with Jack for his clearance of the land.

And so it proved, Bertie declared the agreement null and void, because of the fire and there being no house left standing.

Jack took a large tin of red paint and painted the interesting areas of the statues red.

The statues then became white with black lash streaks from the fire. They also carried red balls.

Jack changed the positions of all six statues so they faced the adjacent bus stop where passengers on the city-bound buses could but stare at wonder at Bertie's red balls.

A furious Bertie soon turned up at Jack's small builder's yard to protest. But Jack said he knew nothing. He had been locked up all night in the garda station when the fire started.

It must have been the heat of the fire turned the balls red, he said.

Bertie countered: "The statues had fig leaves when last I looked."

Jack said: "The fig leaves must have burned away in the fire. Fig leaves are not fire-resistant, at all, at all."

Bertie insisted that Jack come and remove the offending statues; Jack insisted he be paid for everything, in cash and beforehand.

He was paid and the statues returned to pristine white. They were moved to the back of where the house used to stand.

Jack placed them with their tails to the road and left it at that.

In time, he told Bertie, the weeds of pleasure would grow up and cover their shame.

Aunt Ena would understand.

Swimming like a fish

When the long days of summer come in, it seems we all turn towards being a fish, once more.

Some of us go to the seaside.

Some fill up a basin of water and sit in the back garden with bare feet in the cool water and dream of tropical waterfalls.

Some go to the river and swim at the weirs or jump off the head gate and pretend they're jungle explorers.

Others get in a boat and row along the river and try to avoid nesting swans who are not impressed with humans disturbing their nests.

You've never seen a man paddle as fast as when an angry swan stands up on the front of the boat with outstretched wings that cover the horizon and a hissing that would frighten a person out of his life-jacket.

But swans are not the only problem for people who go down to the river to play.

A few summers ago, there were reports of a seal being seen in the river, from time to time.

These reports were dismissed by the authorities for being fanciful and most people agreed that it was a large dog out for a quiet splash and a swim on its own, away from the traffic.

But they were mistaken. The form in the river oftentimes took a human shape and slipped along in the quiet of the evening between the towns of Lucan and Leixlip.

It wasn't a strange apparition or anything like that. It was just Billy doing an imitation of a commando on a special mission.

In the evenings, when Billy thought nobody was watching him, he slipped behind some bushes and became superduck for a while. Like Clark Kent, he left his real world clothes in the bushes and stepped out in his super duper outfit.

Which in Billy's case was his own skin. This state of undress could have led to him being arrested if anybody had seen him; but Billy liked to think he was unseen.

But he was seen and it was his undoing.

On this particular evening he slipped into the water like a predator following its prey.

Or so he thought. To the people watching him from the far bank it was more like he fell in and stayed there, since he was now soaked.

Billy was a low class of a swimmer who liked nothing better than to swim along in a slow crawl with just his eyes above the water like a drowning frog. He popped his mouth up every so often for a deep breath and on he went.

He loved to swim close to the bank and hide in the rushes whenever he spied somebody he knew on the path.

When he was fairly sure they couldn't see him he began to moan in as close an imitation as he could get to a banshee. Though if a banshee sounded that bad she was too sick to be out of bed herself.

Reports of the shape and the sound in the water began to spread through the town and people began to get edgy.

Billy re-told the story to anybody that would listen to him when he was fully dressed and walking around the town. He wanted people to believe there was something there.

Which in a way was his undoing.

For men began to gather together in groups and say they needed to sort out the matter once and for all. They began to keep a watch from behind trees and from the long summer meadow grass.

Billy's other favourite trick was to swim along until he saw someone he knew by name.

He would hide in the water and call their names out in a long olagón that would put fear into the heart of any street fighting dog, never mind the dog's master.

This went on for a while until posses began to form between the two towns.

On a Thursday night in June with a great big flaring sky off to the west, Billy spotted three lads he knew and began calling them out, one at a time, in between ducking beneath the surface to hide, like a feckless monster.

One of them spotted what he swore ever afterwards was the top of the seal's head and shouted at the others to get the stones ready.

Billy couldn't hear under water and when next he surfaced he was surprised to see great big plops of water all about him as a shower of wild stones landed in the river.

The three lads threw with more excitement that accuracy. This was to Billy's advantage for he submerged quickly and headed back downstream.

The stone throwers, when they saw the head of the seal disappear, ran along the bank and threw more stones at the form beneath the water as Billy struck out for home.

Luckily for him they came to an overgrown area and could pursue him no more. Billy came up for air under an overhanging tree when he had left them behind.

They thought he was a seal. Maybe he could call himself Sealman and offer assistance to those in peril on the waters, except he couldn't quite figure out how he'd do that without a stitch of clothes on him.

He might be arrested.

Though he never heard tell of a fish being chastised for swimming naked in the river.

What was good for a fish should be good for a man, Billy thought. But he doubted whether he'd be able to use that as an excuse if it came to court.

He was till thinking it over when he arrived back at his launching point, below the bridge. He was to find that some kind soul had stolen his clothes.

Billy thought that a dog might have run off with his shoes or some of his clothes; but of any of it there was none to be seen.

Naked he was and naked he'd stay.

There was no use in hiding until he saw somebody he knew and asking for the lend of their trousers.

It wasn't the kind of thing men did in Ireland, 21st century or not.

So, he would do the next best thing, he would hide in the bushes until it was dark. At least, that was his intention.

But courting couples came along and Billy knew it was more than his life was worth to be seen in an undressed state, nearby.

He slipped back into the water and there he paddled for what seemed like a year and a day while sweet nothings were exchanged in the glow of a glorious June evening by the bletherers on the bank.

By the time he came out of the water, Billy's skin was as wrinkled as any beached whale might be.

Or a seal for that matter, now that he looked at it.

When they were gone, Billy made his way to the road which, as luck would have it, was quite quiet for the hour of the evening.

He began to run as fast as his wet bare feet would allow. On the way he met every stone on the ground. That made him hop up and down with pain.

It was his yelping and hopping that caused the woman in the end house to look out.

She was one of those women who did not believe in the river monster myth. But looking at a crazed and creased Billy streaking past she decided the town needed a good novena said for the sanity of its people. It was time for old-style religion to return.

Billy got home safely enough, for he lived near the river. He dragged on more clothes than he needed just to reassure himself that all was well, and to warm up.

The following day, the town was full of talk of the naked man and the seal in the river. A protest meeting was called by the local councillors. It called for a helicopter patrol above the river in the interest of safety.

Billy attended the meeting fully dressed. He got himself elected chief security liaison officer with the Garda, on behalf of the residents

For a while, they patrolled the river in boats and Billy offered advice on where to look for himself.

He even had a jaunt in the helicopter when it made its single sweep over the river.

But as hard as he looked Billy could not see himself in the water. Fish or no fish.

He enjoyed the spin in the helicopter so much that he decided he'd buy a hang glider and jump off the bridge to see how far he could fly before he landed in the river.

After all, people watching for a river monster would never think of looking up in the sky, would they?

137

Sleepwalking Lover

There is a way of releasing the asset that is your home in straitened times.

Liam knew this and decided to take in guests to pay the bills. He was in sole occupation of the premises. His wife had left town long ago.

One day he came in from work and found a note on the table saying "I am gone, I will not be back. Your ex-wife."

The last bit was unnecessary, for he knew her handwriting.

So Liam contracted Jack Ladd to do some knocking down of walls and moved into the box-bedroom to live.

Jack constructed an illegal extension in the form of a lean-to toilet and sometime shower room at the side of the house on the ground floor.

The premises now had two guest bedrooms, one with an ensuite bathroom and the other with a split-level bedroom and bathroom.

The disadvantage in occupying suite number two was that if you were short taken in the middle of the night you had to go downstairs, out the door, along the wall, in the door, pull the light cord and shortly thereafter the return journey began.

Liam placed ads in parish newsletters in five surrounding parishes, saying he was willing to take in guests.

He made money as he went along for he developed an approach that allowed for no waste.

He asked everybody, the night before, what they would like for breakfast. All said the full Irish so as to get the best value from the stay.

But Liam refined the offering to ask: "How many rashers would you eat, how many sausages, how many eggs would you manage?"

He bought that amount exactly. It was not the old days when you could buy a few eggs off the counter. Liam bought the minimum quantities allowable at the convenience store and sold the overage to Bridie, his neighbour.

By and by, two lads he had been to school with turned up seeking accommodation.

They were men who had entered their fifth decade on the planet and had decided they no longer wished to live with their wives.

To be more precise, their wives decided they no longer wished to live with them and changed the locks on the front and back doors while the men were out doing what 40-something men do before they go home and make excuses for the state they are in.

The wives attended the same Pilates sessions and when one locked her man out, the second thought this a good idea and did likewise.

Oisín was the first to arrive at Liam's house seeking shelter. Liam looked at him long and hard, for he knew Oisín was not a man well disposed to settling debts.

Liam said he did have a room available. Sadly, the rules and regulations laid down by the competent authority in Brussels said it was money in advance and how many eggs did he eat at breakfast?

It was raining and Oisín was soaked to the skin and the rain was getting into his backpack so he handed Liam an exorbitant amount of money and took possession of the ensuite bedroom for a week.

Two nights later, there was a knock on the door and there was Frank, also with a small bag containing whatever clothes he had been able to recover from the front garden where they landed.

He carried a plastic bag containing his good shoes. They were soaking wet. He had high hopes of returning them to glory once they dried out.

Liam struck the same deal with Frank as he had with Oisín and asked him if he would share a room. At which point Frank became agitated and asked Liam what he thought he was. He was not sharing with any man. If it was a woman it would be different, he laughed.

"Ha ha."

So, Liam rented the second room to Frank, the one with the wandering bathroom.

The men stayed and paid rent and worked somewhere all day and returned at night. They were civil to one another for all three had played on the parish team when they were under-14s.

It was a big moment therefore when Frank suggested to Liam that he might bring a woman home to his room for an overnight and how would that be?

Frank had determined that if he was no longer allowed sleep at home he might as well sleep with whomever he could.

Liam, sensing opportunity, said he could pay for double occupancy for a week even if his luck only held for the one night.

Frank countered: "You should reduce my weekly rent if I sleep elsewhere for a night or two and don't eat any of your eggs, rashers or sausages, not to mention the fried bread."

A stalemate was reached. Then it was agreed that the woman in question could stay the night, for no extra charge, provided she was quiet about it and did not eat breakfast. Frank would continue to pay the full whack for his room and breakfast the following day whether he slept there or not.

In none of which was Oisín consulted. If he had been then disaster could have been averted.

Oisín by now was participating in marriage counselling with his wife and was hoping to re-take possession of the marital home. In due course, he had every intention of locking his wife out. He would cite as good reason her messing about with the young locksmith who had locked Oisín out in the first place.

Negotiations were proceeding apace; but Oisín had still not been granted conjugal visiting rights. He had not, despite his wife's claims to the contrary, been playing offside.

By now, he had stored up a certain amount of anxiety that would be welcomed by several females of the town if he were he to call on them, night or day.

But he did not.

On this wild wet night when Frank brought Karen home to Liam's house, Oisín had retired to bed early for an early start the next morning in work.

Karen was a woman of their own age who cared little for who she went with so long as fun was had by all.

Frank said he agreed that fun should be had.

Frank and Karen had fun that night and more than a few drinks. Frank fell asleep at the excitement of it all. But not before he had forgotten to tell her that the bathroom was downstairs, out the door, and around the back of the house.

Karen found a door open in the upper hall for Jack Ladd had left the original door to the bathroom in place when he smashed a new door into the master bedroom to form an ensuite bathroom. Karen took possession.

The ensuite was like a bus station; you could come and go by whatever door you liked.

It was not Karen's fault that once her time was up she returned to Frank's bedroom by the wrong door.

The room was as dark as a coal cellar in November.

Karen said later that she could not be faulted for tumbling into a bed where a man lay sleeping soundly. When she left Frank he was asleep, when she re-entered a bedroom from the bathroom its occupant was asleep and snoring.

She swore to the gardaí that she thought it was Frank in the bed when she began to tickle his fancy.

Oisín, aroused from the depths of slumber by a guiding hand, thought he was home again and swung into action after a long enforced abstinence.

Karen was delighted with the renewed vigour of her lover. She had thought all was spent. She called Frank's name out loudly as matters proceeded.

It was not long before a roaring Frank burst through the door and began punching the startled Oisín in the bed.

Oisín, in turn, did his best to pull Frank's head off his shoulders, once he re-gained focus.

Karen screamed loudly since it was by no means sure who would win and claim her for his own.

It was great.

Liam arrived with a hurley to calm matters and the scrap was very soon a tri-cornered affair.

Somebody passing by outside used a mobile phone to tell the gardaí that a woman seemed to be attacking three men in a dark bedroom.

All four of them spent the night in the Garda station before the men appeared in court with Karen as the witness; but witness to what she wasn't sure, she said, because it was pitch dark, and all she saw was bodies.

Neither was the judge sure as to what had happened.

It was obvious from the men that they had tried to take each other's life as best they could; but nobody knew who hit who when and how many times, so the judge bound them all to the peace and sent them home.

Liam told the other two to leave. Each said they wouldn't stay and demanded their money back for the following week.

Liam gave it to them. Then Karen asked if she could stay on and offered to work around the house in exchange for rent.

She remembered Liam was a hurler and how well he made a puck out when his blood was up.

If there was one thing she liked and it was a good man with a puck, she said.

Liam said yes for he needed company himself and he wanted to see Karen in the light, for a change, to see how it would go.

Making a Gig

When Kenny was a boy he dreamed of driving the fastest gig in town.

He wanted to be the winner of the races that happened every summer on the high hill out of town.

Gigs, for those unschooled in the science of locomotion, were made of a plank of wood and four wheels. The front wheels were attached to a cross beam operated by a pivot in the form of a large bolt at the front of the plank.

A rope, sometimes braided from several strains of hairy twine purloined from many sources, was attached to the stub axles of the front wheels, an arrangement that meant the driver had steering control of the gig in motion.

There were no brakes. They were considered a luxury to the serious gig owner. Brakes on a gig were like jewellery on an elephant. Out of place and more than a little bit silly.

Either a driver knew what he was doing or he did not. If he did not, then he shouldn't be in control of a gig in the first place. Everybody knew that.

Some gig owners liked to do away with the steering rope altogether and preferred to guide their fortunes with their feet.

In that case, the front axle was designed to allow room for the sole of a foot to be placed on either side of the front axle. It was then simply a matter of pushing on the right if you wanted to go left and vice versa.

In the event that the gig moved too fast, and took a mind of its own, and no amount of steering or applying the sole of a foot to the racing wheels would slow it down, there was an emergency procedure in place. It was only to be used as a last resort.

If there was a flat piece of ground anywhere in the near vicinity, the driver --- always allowing that he kept his nerve sufficiently to carry out the manoeuvre properly --- would aim for the safe area. He would pull the gig to the left, if the evacuation area was to the right, let the gig slide sideways in a semi-controlled skid and at the last moment the driver would roll off onto the ground.

He'd continue rolling sideways in contact with the ground until velocity slowed, gravity took over and he came to a halt.

If he was lucky he stopped before he hit a wall. If he was not, then the wall hit him. A sliding driver usually aimed for contact with his shoulder as the best option. Nobody had the luxury of a safety helmet at this stage in man's evolution.

Very rarely was a visit to a hospital required.

More often the gig was damaged in some shape or form and needed to be upended to be repaired in situ.

It all passed for sport. There was an echo of the rivalry that existed then in a recent planning case before the Planning Appeals Board and the courts.

Kenny had a great rival in Dermot K who always seemed to be there or thereabouts when it came to which gig racer could drag a gig highest on the hill before letting loose on a wild descent through hordes of enthusiastic spectators. Like the bull runners of Pamplona they really wished to see blood and gore and did not overcare who was first home or who travelled the furthest on the flat road at the foot of the hill.

Gig racing died away as prosperity arrived and people found deposits for secondhand cars and life took over. There was an engine and brakes and a door that closed. Oh bliss.

Kenny married and settled down in a house directly across the road from Dermot K who had also married.

Both men were friends, as always. They were rivals. According as one progressed in life the other did his best to match him.

As in gigs, so in cars. Kenny was the first to have a car and when Dermot K caught up with his own car ---which was a bit more recent and bigger than Kenny's --- Kenny decided he needed to do something.

Kenny thought about it for a while and called in Jack Ladd who is the town's handyman and general contractor, when he feels like it.

Kenny bought a small Peugeot 107 that was not all that old. He thought a fine garage would be the thing to have. He awarded the contract to Jack.

Jack built a garage around the car where it stood. It was parked behind the house on the boundary between the drive and the grasslands that formed the back garden.

It was a fine structure and even had an up and over garage door which Kenny took pleasure in slamming down at night to signal that his car was safely locked away.

Then Dermot K built a garage in the side garden that was attached to his house by a utility room from which the sound of a washing machine in motion could be heard.

A car, a garage, a washing machine, and a utility room, in one go.

Kenny was at a loss as to what to do. He considered buying a large plastic swimming pool and burying it in the back garden as an indoor swimming house pool once he found a roof for it.

That plan was suddenly put on hold for Kenny had a bit of luck that people only dream about.

A quick pick on the lottery showed up in the winning numbers. Kenny now had a safe amount of disposable income with which to buy a more prestigious version of his car. He was not suddenly rich by any means; but he had some cash to splash about.

And so he arrived home with a brand new Peugeot 607 and parked it in the drive so that Dermot K could see it well. The smaller car was gone. Traded in.

A problem arose when Kenny drove the new car into the garage for the night.

It was significantly longer than his first car and the garage door would not close on it.

There it was.

The boot and the back passenger doors were exposed to the elements and Dermot K, when he saw what had happened, made great sport of the dilemma that Kenny now found himself in.

Kenny sent for Jack Ladd and gave out to him for building the garage to the exact dimensions of a small car.

Jack Ladd said he'd sort it out, no problem. He would do so while Kenny was away on a foreign holiday with his family, on his winnings.

From his holiday location, Kenny emailed a never-ending series of digital pictures to Dermot K of the holiday as it progressed. He always added that he wished that Dermot K was there as well.

When Kenny returned, he was pleasantly surprised to find the garage door now closed down on the larger Peugeot 607 without colliding with it.

He was less than pleased when he discovered how this was achieved.

Jack Ladd had simply removed enough blocks from the back wall of the garage to allow the front of the car to be parked in the back garden while the rest sat inside the garage and nestled against the up and over door.

"QED," Jack said.

Dermot K held his tongue for somebody else had complained to the planning authorities.

The structure had no planning permission front or rear, up or over, or in the back garden.

Kenny went a bit mad after that and used his lottery winnings to hire professionals to argue his case for retention of the drive-through garage.

Which is how it ended up in court.

Jack Ladd removed the roof from the garage and they argued, in vain, that what was left were two piles of blocks standing opposite one another connected by a second hand door for a bit of privacy.

It was no use however, the whole lot had to come down, and so it did, to utter silence from Dermot K who had taken the precaution of getting planning permission for his garage, before he built it.

The last straw came when Dermot K wheeled out a brand new go-kart and told Kenny that he was taking up the sport at Mondello racetrack.

"Just like the old days but with an engine for going up hills," he said.

Dermot K was not surprised to hear, a little later, that Kenny was waiting for delivery of a second-hand go-kart he bought on eBay.

It was said the machine had been used by a Formula-I champion for practice driving.

But the seller would not sign an affidavit to that effect, when asked by Kenny.

Dermot K heard Kenny asking if you could drive a go-kart down the motorway to Mondello, or not, without number plates.

It was the sort of question that gave Dermot K sleepless nights as he awaited the dawn and the roar of engines as the open road beckoned, once more.

Dead woman haunts ball player

A N unmarried woman, a neighbour's growing boy and a bouncing ball don't usually get along. But when Arlene passed away not long after saying to Teddy that she would haunt him as soon as she died, Teddy the boy was understandably terrified.

Especially when a voice began calling him from the darkness outside his October window, not long after the funeral, and a hand dragged fingernails against the windowpane.

Teddy revelled in his football. He was a member of the local team and managed to keep his place on it, most of the time.

He practiced and practiced as hard and as long as he could so as to be match fit at all times.

Arlene, for her part, lived in a single-storey cottage with her sister Bernice across the road from Teddy and his family.

To practice ball control Teddy and his pals played squares on the road between the houses. They bounced the ball against the wall to field a return shot.

The effect inside Arlene's house, she said, was like being in a tar barrel with somebody whacking it with a stick.

Arlene and Bernice ran a small sweet shop from their home; not for profit, it cost them money to do so; but because a daft aunt had left them the house on condition that the sweet shop be kept open, forever.

Arlene had a day job. Bernice was what they used to call delicate. Which really meant she was as mad as a badger having inherited her aunt's mad genes.

Neither were married, Bernice because she trusted no man; for she thought they wanted to get their hands on her sweets.

Arlene had a job that supported both of them. Unlike Arlene, she had a love life with a human being. Bernice, for her part, fantasised about Snickers bars.

Arlene's love life was with a married chap from accounts, called Stewart, who promised to leave home, his wife Ellan, and set up with Bernice; sometime.

Arlene looked after his extra marital needs and he took her away on occasional conference weekends through the year.

None of which quite fulfilled Arlene's dreams of a happy family life.

Looking at Teddy and his pals she thought she was better off without a family of children to bother about.

As days grew shorter Teddy and the boys spent more time on the road bouncing the ball between them where the ground was both firm and dry. The ball bounced on the road in a monotonous whack that repeated itself at regular intervals.

Arlene was looking forward to the bank-holiday weekend with Stewart at a conference in London especially organised to match the Irish day off on Monday.

They would leave on Friday morning and come back on Monday evening. It would be like a week off together as man and wife.

She would ask the waiter in the hotel restaurant to come back to take the order when: "My husband has had a chance to study it in more detail." Stewart would order the wine and say: "My wife will have the house special."

Things would be as they should be in real life, as they were inside Arlene's mind.

But Stewart's wife declared, late in the day, that she would accompany Stewart on the trip to Edinburgh on Ryanair. She needed a break, the fare was low and they could have a second honeymoon and get it together again, she said with no conviction at all.

Arlene was devastated. Stewart apologised and said that Arlene could come as well. She could learn things in Edinburgh that would stand to her in work.

She might get promoted to Stewart's level and they would be colleagues and have to travel to meetings in Navan and Monagahan and places like that.

It would give them opportunity to be together; even if they couldn't stay overnight in any of these places, with plausible reason.

Arlene told Stewart what she thought of his ideas and the situation she found herself in. She went further and issued an ultimatum to Stewart along the lines of choosing between her and his present situation.

Arlene never addressed Ellen by name. She might be Stewart's wife; but to Arlene she was the situation.

This time, the situation won. Arlene was wrong-footed. She stayed at home.

When the bouncing ball got to her once more, she said something to Teddy and the boys playing football on the street outside the sweetshop that she regretted, almost immediately she said it.

"I'll haunt you, Teddy. You'll never sleep again, when I die," she said.

Arlene felt better for saying something to somebody that made them feel worse than she did. But she regretted saying that to Teddy; for the bouncing of the ball stopped immediately.

There was a silence on the road that Arlene admitted was eerie and a forecast of what might come now that the curse was uttered aloud.

The other boys went home. Teddy held onto the ball on his hip with one hand holding it in place. He turned for home and hid the ball beneath the stairs at the back in his hiding place. It could stay there. Everyone knew the two mad sisters were witches and a witch's curse was not something to take lightly.

Arlene tried to put her intemperate outburst behind her and started on a stock check of the shop. Fat Bernice ate so many sweets during a day that Arlene had long ago ordered in an extra order of chocolate that she carried on the stock list. But she they knew no longer existed in their original form.

It was to be her final stock check.

Arlene accidently choked herself to death in the back of the sweetshop when sucking a large gobstopper.

It was her own fault; she had been mulling over what she should have said to Stewart and she expressed her thoughts aloud.

She became agitated by his imaginary answers and responded angrily. But she took a deep breath and blocked her windpipe with the gobstopper.

Bernice found her the following morning as stiff as a stick of souvenir rock.

Teddy was inconsolable during and after the funeral for he knew that he had caused Arlene's death by bouncing the ball against her wall.

His mother told him not to be silly. To calm him as best she could she brought him over to the closed sweetshop with the black wreath upon the door and asked Bernice to speak to him.

This made matters worse. Bernice now knew who had killed Arlene. Sweets would never kill you, she told her sister often enough in the past; now she had proof.

But she told Teddy's mammy that Teddy was being silly and of course Arlene would forgive him for bouncing the ball against her wall before she died, if she was around now to say so.

"But she isn't 'cause she's dead."

Teddy slept in the ground floor room nearest the road and made sure the curtains were well closed when he went to bed.

Still, closed curtains or not, he heard the ould one call his name. It was Arlene back from the dead, to haunt him.

"Teddy....Teddy...." came the voice in a pitch that rose and fell.

He was terrified.

It came again: "Teddy...Teddy..."

A hand dragged finger nails across the glass beyond the pulled curtains and Teddy was about to expire for lack of air in his lungs, on account of his screaming.

His babbling mother came charging in, and dragged the curtains from the window to expose a dark empty street with not a soul to be seen.

This went on for a week with no sleep for anybody to be had. Teddy's mammy was getting very cross and said that she would have liked to have choked Arlene herself.

Mothers have a way of bringing matters to a head.

The haunting ended a week after Arlene's funeral when Teddy's mammy emptied a pot of yellow paint from the upstairs window onto the head of the mad window scratcher who ran away into the night howling that she was blinded for sure.

There was no more haunting after that. Teddy's mammy told Bernice that if any yellow coloured ghosts turned up again she would seek to have the shop closed as a public nuisance. Bernice would be committed to hospital as a sweet-eating child-haunting barking-mad lunatic.

Peace of a sort came back again; but Teddy who could have played soccer for Ireland took up snooker.

It is after all an indoor game played with balls under lights; with not a mad sweetshop to be seen anywhere.

Stuck in a rut

There is a tide in the affairs of man that is sometimes best left alone. There is a cycle to nature that continues whether man plays a part in it or not.

Deer will mate in Phoenix Park as they have done for centuries even if the parked motor car of an amorous couple will not start.

Adam was sure the car he bought was roadworthy. The man said it was and said he would post him the NCT certificate as soon as he found it; after all a cash deal is a cash deal and deserves the best attention of the seller, no doubt about that.

Adam invited Kate for a spin in his new car. He and Kate knew one another, on and off; but this was the first time he had asked her out; after all when all you have is a bicycle; it's hard to ask a girl if she would like to come for a spin.

Adam gave up asking after one too many refusals.

But the car was different and changed things. Kate was the first person he asked out, and she agreed, more or less straightaway. The days of chasing girls on a bike were over, as far as Adam was concerned.

Days had grown shorter and nights were longer, which suited Adam; for the lights on the car definitely worked and he accepted no boundaries to where he could travel in daylight or in darkness. The car was his and he was for the high road.

Kate was ready for their date on the corner of her road when he drove around. Adam flashed his lights once, and tipped the horn in greeting.

She hopped in and buckled up. For a moment, his hand touched denim when he reached over to make sure the door was properly secured.

"Don't want to lose you on the bends," he said.

"Will you be going fast then?" she asked in a voice that promised much to an excited Adam.

"I'll go as fast as you like," he said and slipped the car into gear. They were off.

Adam invested as much as he could in a tank of petrol. He could travel as far as he liked and he would still have enough fuel to get home again. He said as much to Kate who was impressed without knowing why she should be impressed.

Still, he was trying to be nice.

They drove for ages. Adam avoided traffic tailbacks for the most part. He asked if Kate would care to take a final trip through Phoenix Park before they turned for home?

He made it sound like the voyage to the New World of St Brendan in a currach. All he was short of doing was lowering the window to see which way the wind blew.

Twilight had descended on the public park when Adam took the scenic route along the Upper Glen Road. He told Kate a little about the park for he had consulted a very good website on the park before he ventured out.

He was able to tell Kate about the glen and how it got its name of the Furry Glen from the furze that grew there in abundance at one time. He told her the present day deer herd was descended from animals brought there in the 17th century to form a royal deer herd. He told her that this time of the year, October or so, was the mating season for the deer.

Kate said when Adam began to describe the harems that the dominant bucks drew around them: "I think it should be one male for one female, for life."

This was great news, as far as Adam was concerned. He was on a winner.

"I agree with you," he said as he turned the car onto the Furze Road and headed towards Oldtown Wood. The wood formed the periphery of the 200-acre Fifteen Acres that several hundred deer called home.

The road was cut in two to make two adjoining cul de sacs and there were a number of cars parked on the side of the road with their windows steamed up.

Adam parked the car; but Kate said she was uncomfortable being here.

"Would you prefer to just watch the deer?" Adam asked.

"Yes, I would," Kate said without realising what Adam had in mind.

He started up the car once more. The music dipped on the CD player when he did so. He drove forward at some speed to cross over an earthen barrier and before Kate knew where she was they were off the road and heading along a squelching track towards the open spaces of deerland. She was not happy.

"Where are we going?" asked Kate as she peered into the gathering darkness of Oldtown Wood.

"To see the deer," said Adam. "I thought you wanted to see the deer."

"I can't see deer in the dark. I can't see anything in the dark, "she answered in a voice that rose in pitch as they bumped along the track beside the trees.

Even a man as highly excited as Adam could see that Kate was not for deer watching this evening.

He slowed the car and could feel the back wheels slewing around as they crossed a pool of surface water. It would be best to keep driving, he thought, otherwise he might not be able to get going again.

But Kate had had enough and she said so. "Pull in here and stop, please," she said. Please was not said in the usual way we would say please. It was a command to do or die.

Adam saw his night of romance fading fast. He spun the wheel to bring the car to a throbbing halt with the headlights facing the grassy expanse of the Fifteen Acres where not a single deer was to be seen in the lights.

Adam's idea of deer herd movement was a remembered image of great herds of migrating animals heading for feeding grounds in Canada somewhere, seen on a television programme.

Here there was just blackness and white light where the headlights shone on nothing.

The deer were there. But quite sensibly they were settling down for a rest and a sleep now that day was done.

Adam spoke softly to Kate and re-assured her that they were quiet safe where they were. Kate, feeling a little silly now that they were parked and that nobody seemed to be approaching the car with an axe to attack them allowed Adam to place his arm around her shoulders. She allowed him to kiss her and after a while she got into the rhythm of the evening and began to enjoy his attentions a bit more.

Adam popped on a CD of romantic mood music and they sat in the car with the headlights pouring illumination down a narrow beam of light.

They soon forgot about life outside the car. They were too busy.

Now, it is a fact that during the mating season of deer the strongest prevail. It seems that females appreciate this. The strongest bucks attract the most attention during the annual rut.

To show they are the strongest and to advertise their availability, the bucks bellow a long deep throaty roar that when experienced in daylight is impressive; but when heard when darkness surrounds you like a cloak is very disturbing.

The car's headlights attracted a particularly cross buck who came along to stand directly in the beam at the bonnet of the car.

He bellowed as deep and as loud a bellow as he could, fulfilling his role as a rampant male protecting what was his.

Adam was so far gone by now that a train could have sounded its whistle and he would not have noticed. But a jittery Kate looked over Adam's shoulder. She began to scream as loudly as the air in her lungs would allow her.

Adam thought she was just pleased at the experience of love-making with him in his new second-hand car. Her screaming was a bit much though. He would have to speak to her about it, later when they had both calmed down.

When she continued screaming and began to beat his ears with her fists Adam looked up to see what was wrong. Things were getting out of hand. A little screaming was one thing; but thumping him was another.

He began to scream himself when he saw the buck staring through the windscreen at the mating humans.

"Get him away," said Kate.

"How?" asked a frightened Adam.

"Say shoo, or something. Get him away, or drive over him," said Kate now that survival of the human was at stake.

"You can't just drive over a deer," said Adam who was beginning to wonder if he really knew Kate at all.

"Blow the bloody horn, then," she said.

Adam blew the horn, which didn't seem to his ears to be as full blooded as it should be.

He switched off the lights to see if that would help and the horn sounded louder alright; but when he turned the lights back on he discovered that the buck had moved around and was staring at him through the driver's window.

Adam screamed, Kate screamed, the buck bellowed, and from the CD player Tony Bennett reported that he had left his heart in San Francisco.

"Drive off," Kate shouted. "Drive now."

But the car was not for driving for if the car was second-hand then the battery had been touched by more hands than a candidate in an election could encounter.

It gave up the ghost. Try as he might, Adam could raise no more than a wheeze from the engine.

The lights worked after a fashion and Adam heard the car door slam as Kate left him and his car to the buck's amorous advances.

She ran down the beam of light until she could see no more. She kept going into the darkness and headed south for the turnstile at Chapelizod and the shop lights of civilisation.

Adam, in darkness and in an attempt to brew power in the battery, rolled up the windows and switched off everything while he waited for the buck to go away.

He rang Kate's mobile but there was no answer. Wherever she was, his call was not being returned.

He rang the motor rescue service; but the dispatcher hung up on him when he said he was in the middle of a wood on the outskirts of the Fifteen Acres. A rampant buck deer was in the way and the battery was down too low to start the car and was there any chance of getting somebody to come and give him a jump in the park?

The phone was silenced.

Since he could not walk away in case Kate returned to the car, and he didn't want to take a chance himself of meeting more buck deer on the trail of romance Adam passed a cold night in the car.

Kate was polite to him ever after but Adam noticed that she moved away when he approached her. His father was not impressed when he had to turn out to tow the car out of the morass it was in.

He said so to Adam.

If there is a tide in the affairs of man that taken at its flood leads on to greater things, then Adam had missed the boat.

.

Fathers are forever

Without fathers there would be no human race and that's the long and short of it. Luke's father died at a time when he was least expecting it, and since Luke's mother was gone ahead, this made Luke into an orphan at the age of 35 years.

So, when he read that an American gent was coming to the town hall to speak about being a man Luke decided to go along to that.

He had a good shower and picked out his best jeans and top and off he went...only to find the doors were locked.

Teresa saw he had his best clean clothes on him so she shouted at him. "That real man missed the plane."

Luke pretended he didn't hear her and began to read the notices on the notice board about single mothers' entitlements and free breast checks.

He even rooted in his pockets for the butt of a pencil to show he was really a seeker after information. He'd take notes.

But Teresa wanted to go home and she didn't want to leave Luke on the premises behind her, so she said.

"That American will be here tomorrow night at the same time. He said to tell anybody that turns up that he's sorry and that while real men don't really say sorry, he would make an exception this time. Does that make sense to you and the other real men, Luke?"

Luke went home and hung up the good clothes and watched a video. He sat in his boxer shorts so that he wouldn't crease his good gear.

The next night he went to the town hall again. He was prepared to walk past and go on over to the pub for the night if there was no sign of anybody but Teresa there.

But the American; whose name was Steve, had been on Liffey Sound FM the night before on a link from America and loads of people turned up to hear him.

Luke was lucky to get a seat. He found a place in the second row beside a famous national radio personality.

Luke was flustered to see so many women at a man's affirmation meeting until he realised that these particular women were mostly on the hunt for male flesh.

Steve felt sorry for them.

None of which would have mattered except for what happened as the evening progressed.

Steve declared he was a leader of the men's movement. It was time, according to Steve, that men asserted themselves. Since Father's Day was about to fall on Sunday it was a fine time for men to re-discover their masculinity.

This sounded a bit dodgy until Luke looked at the famous man beside him who was nodding sagely at Steve's pronouncements.

Luke relaxed a little to listen to Steve who was doing a fine job of pacing the floor.

He was like a cur that smelled a bitch in heat in the next parish and wanted out of the room to be about his masculine duties. He paced so far and so fast that Luke gave up trying to watch him with his eyes. He closed his eyes and watched him with his ears.

He was horrified to discover, a short time later, that he had fallen asleep and when he awoke his head was on the famous man's chest.

It didn't seem to bother the famous man who just smiled at Luke until Luke sat up straight again.

He began to wonder why he had never heard of the famous man's wife, nor for that matter could he recall the famous man's name being linked to any women. Naturally, he began to wonder if the man liked men more than women. It would explain a lot.

Then he began to wonder if Steve was gay. Steve was smiling at him waiting for an answer to some question he had asked.

It was the question that had awoken Luke, he now realised; but he could not recall the actual question.

"I'll pass," he said in a low voice.

"I understand, Luke, that you don't want to speak about your first sexual awakening, at this stage. I hope that by the end of this session you will be able to stand before us and tell us what it was like for you as a young man," said Steve from his full height in the middle of the floor.

160

The famous man smiled at Luke and his future courage. Steve then began asking people in the packed room what they wanted of him.

Luke understood Steve was supposed to be telling them what he thought and how they could be better at something or other. After all, he was a leader of men, according to himself.

Weren't leaders supposed to lead?

Questions came from the body of the hall and while most were from men; Steve allowed questions from the women present. Luke noted that Steve did not attempt to answer any questions at all.

He just repeated the question and said: "We'll put that on the top shelf for now and we'll come back to it later," And he made a gesture of placing it on a high shelf.

Given that Steve was a good deal taller than six feet in his high heeled leather boots it made Luke think that it was a very high shelf indeed.

Steve began to explain that all he told them was to be found in his books and CDs which were on sale at the back of the room.

Luke turned and saw that Teresa was now the bookseller. It was unlikely many would make it out of the room without at least one signed copy of a book.

But Luke couldn't figure out what it was that Steve had told them. He wondered how long he had been asleep?

When Luke pulled up his sleeve to check the time on his father's wristwatch he triggered something in Steve. The leader declared the gathering was coming to the half-way stage and they would soon break up into teams of four people.

He said he would prefer if the women present would spread themselves around the groups, freely.

Luke could see several women nodding happily. That was what they were here for. To be free and to spread themselves about.

Steve said all present should reveal to one another in-group how they had felt during their first physical experience with another person outside their family.

He smiled at Luke.

There was a shuffling in the room as groups formed. Luke used the confusion to make his way from the room and was half way home when whatever madness Steve was proposing was taking place in the second half.

Luke never heard tell of Steve after that night. He was the leader of the men's movement but he was nowhere to be found.

He asked about the famous man that he'd sat beside and was told he was deaf as a post on the side that Luke had been sitting on. That was the reason he was nodding sagely. He couldn't hear a thing.

But, the following Sunday Luke heard him on national radio talking about this man who had sat beside him; who had been hypnotised and legged it at the break, so terrified was he of the approaching women.

Luke was outraged for a few days; but didn't know how to contact the famous man to tell him so.

A funny thing happened in the town in the days that followed. Teresa began to smile more at him when he passed by on the way to the pub.

Even though there had been other men there; people began to say that Luke was a real man. Women smiled at him and men nodded when he passed by.

Luke couldn't figure it out.

Maybe he had been hypnotised; but how would you know?

Something had happened and he had made somebody very happy. Steve had been impressed, anyway. The famous man had nodded at him, and now there was the change in Teresa.

After a while, Steve began to think he was indeed a real man.

He wondered if he shouldn't become a father himself and pass on some of his greatness to a son.

The only problem was he would need a willing woman.

For without a mother there could be no father.

And that was that.

Real men or no real men.

And Teresa was busy. She told Luke so when next he said hello.

The Silver Wolves Ride Again

Johnny the binman used to observe who was keeping to Lent or not by keeping an eye on the contents of their bins as they were emptied on bin-day.

"Show me his bin, and I'll show you the man," Johnny was fond of saying, though with the arrival of wheely bins and mechanical hoists to lift them into the maw of the refuse truck, there's not half the opportunity to observe life as there was.

Not so long ago, he found a medal on the road when he was returning a bin in the general direction of the house whence it had come.

He knocked on a few doors but nobody was at home.

Or at least they didn't answer his ring on the door. Perhaps they thought he was asking for a Happy Easter gift for the binman.

Either way, he finished up putting the medal in his pocket and having it valued later by Matty the driver from the far road. Matty was the depot expert on all things.

Matty said it was worthless in cash terms but there might be a reward if he put an ad in the newsletter to say it was in safe keeping.

Johnny was sorry when he followed the advice. Several middle-aged men soon claimed the medal as their own.

While it was strange that each could identify the medal down to the last detail, it was obvious that not all could own the medal.

"Maybe, the award was an annual affair and each won in succeeding years and he thought the medal he held was the one they had been presented with?" Johnny suggested to Matty.

The final tally was six men all claiming ownership of the silver talisman.

Some were mild enough about it; some were quite firm that it was theirs and some just threatened him with a call late some night by friends of theirs who were connected.

What they were connected to was never made clear and Johnny ignored them.

Matty said he should call a meeting in a neutral pub and see who made the best case. He offered to be the adjudicator on the understanding that he'd pay for no drink at all during the evening.

The bargain was struck and all assembled on the due date in the designated public bar and lounge.

It soon became clear that all the men were of the same age give or take a few months one way or another.

It was also clear that they knew one another, had something in common, and were at war and had been for many a year.

Matty was a shop steward and well used to hopeless cases. After he and Johnny had a few drinks he slipped into negotiation mode.

He established the six were the surviving members of a rhythm 'n blues band that had played together for a brief time when each of the pot-bellied grandfathers had been teenagers.

The band had been called The Wolves and they had entered for a talent contest in a local cinema when cinemas were trying out any alternative to closure in the face of declining attendances.

The Wolves were fronted by Jack the Man. But Jack passed on to the great gig in the sky following a bad trip in London one fine Lent.

He went, he tripped, he never came back. He's in orbit still.

A consequence of the unplanned demise of the frontman was that the band went their separate ways.

Until now.

Matty soon discovered, on Johnny's behalf, that the award the Wolves received in the talent competition was a single silver medal.

They were the only group in the contest that could afford a set of drums and the noise that Al the drummer created was enough to win them the medal.

There were seven members in the band. Possession of the medal would rotate on a weekly turnover with Jack having it for two weeks because he was the lead and only singer.

Then, on account of the bad London trip, he was the late lead and only singer. The medal went missing somewhere between week four and six; nobody was quite sure when.

What everybody was quite sure about was that each and every one of them was entitled to the medal, in perpetuity.

Matty suggested they rotate the medal. Nobody would agree on who was to stand in for Jack or hold onto the medal for two weeks.

This was when Matty's genius became apparent. He saw the solution quite early on; but since there was still an amount of drink left in the barman's taps he held his whist until they had exhausted their arguments.

Matty explained his plan to Johnny and they went back to the six of one and half a dozen of another's that were still arguing while still not talking to one another about a medal.

They stopped arguing. Matty asked if he and Johnny could join the band that had not played together in 40 years.

That way, he and Johnny would take the medal for one each of Jack's two weeks and rotation would be restored. They would toss a coin to see who would start it off again.

In the euphoria that followed it was agreed amongst the Wolves that Johnny should hold the medal for the first week to be followed by Matty and so on until the round was completed.

And since Matty could not sing or play music to save his life, it was agreed that he be the new manager and be paid a percentage of the reformed band's income.

The band would now be the Silver Wolves and Johnny would be the road manager. Johnny agreed. After all, if there was one thing that Johnny understood it was roads and trucks and moving stuff around.

What he decided to keep to himself for the time being was the location of the house outside of which he had found the medal.

There is after all a binman's code. If somebody's girlfriend threw out the medal as being worthless to her, then Johnny was not telling.

What happens in showbiz, stays in showbiz, as Jack the Man would have said, if he had stayed alive long enough.

From that day on, Johnny paid special attention to the ground around the bins he emptied.

You never know what you may find, if you keep an eye open.